GIANT BOOK OF MATH FUN

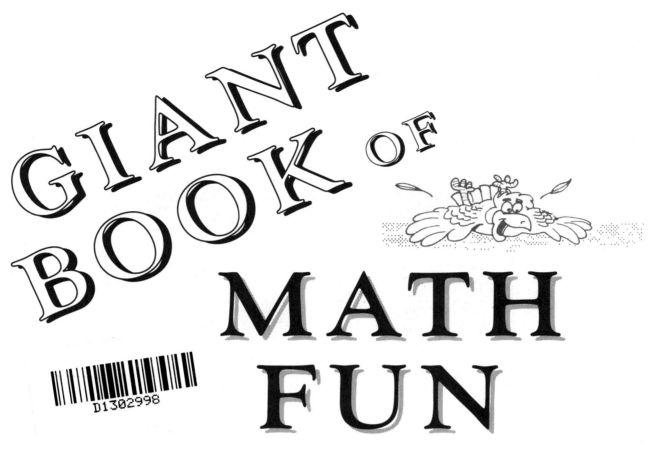

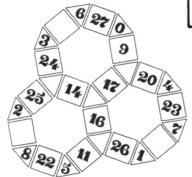

Raymond Blum, Glen Vecchione,
Kurt Smith, Steve Ryan &
Adam Hart-Davis

Sterling Publishing Co., Inc. New York

10 9 8 7 6 5 4 3 2 1
Published by Sterling Publishing Company, Inc.
387 Park Avenue South, New York, N.Y. 10016
Material in this collection was adapted from
Amazing Math Puzzles © 1998 Adam Hart-Davis
Math Challenges © 1997 Glen Vecchione
Math Logic Puzzles © 1996 Kurt Smith
Math Tricks, Puzzles & Games © 1994 Raymond Blum
Mathemagic © 1991 Raymond Blum
Mystifying Math Puzzles © 1996 Steve Ryan
Test Your Math IQ © 1994 Steve Ryan

Distributed in Canada by Sterling Publishing
c/o Canadian Manda Group, One Atlantic Avenue, Suite 105
Toronto, Ontario, Canada M6K 3E7
Distributed in Australia by Capricorn Link (Australia) Pty Ltd
P.O. Box 6651, Baulkham Hills, Business Centre, NSW 2153, Australia
Distributed in Great Britain and Europe by Chris Lloyd
463 Ashley Road, Parkstone, Poole, Dorset, BH14 0AX, United Kingdom

Sterling ISBN 0-8069-9465-7

Contents

MATHEMAGIC

MATH PUZZLES & GAMES

MATHEMAGIC

CHAPTER ONE
ARITHMETRICKS

Arithmetricks

These amazing number tricks are fun to watch and even more fun to perform for others. They are easy to learn and, if you follow the steps carefully, they practically work themselves.

Practice a trick until you have successfully worked it through two or three times. Then you are ready to perform it for your friends. Be sure to work the trick *slowly* so that you don't make careless errors.

Remember, magicians never reveal their secrets. When someone asks you how you did a trick, just say, "Very well!" Also, don't repeat a trick for the same person. They might figure out how you did the trick if they see it a second time. Show them another trick instead and they will be even more amazed!

COIN CAPER

Your friend removes some coins from a bowl when your back is turned. After performing some number magic, you are able is disclose the number of coins that are hidden in her hand!

Materials

20 coins   A small bowl

Presentation	**Example**

1. Put a bowl of 20 coins on the table, and then turn your back. Ask your friend to remove any number of coins from 1 to 9 and put them in her pocket.

She removes 7 coins

2. Tell her to count the number of coins that remain in the bowl.

20 – 7 = 13 remain

3. Ask her to find the sum of the digits of that number.

13 → 1 + 3 = 4

4. Tell her to remove that number of coins from the bowl and put those in her pocket too.

She removes 4 more coins

5. Ask her to remove any number of coins from the bowl and hide them in her *hand*.

She hides 6

6. When you turn around, take one of the coins out of the bowl. Hold it to your forehead and pretend to be in deep thought for a few seconds. Then reveal the number of coins that your friend is hiding in her hand!

How to Do it

When you turn around, secretly count the number of coins that remain in the bowl. Just subtract that number from 9. That difference is the number of coins that she is hiding in her hand!

9 – 3 coins in the bowl = 6 coins in her hand

An Exception

If your friend hides 9 coins in her hand and there are no coins left in the bowl, hold the bowl to your forehead.

The Secret

This trick uses a mathematical procedure called casting out nines. The first subtraction results in a number between 10 and 20. Any number between 10 and 20 minus the sum of its digits always equals 9.

A Variation

You can also tell her how many coins are in her pocket. It will always be 11!

Riddle Me

Why are 1980 U.S. pennies worth almost $20.00?

1,980 pennies = $19.80, which is almost $20.00!

NUMBER SPIRITS

Your friend randomly chooses any 3-digit number, and then works a few problems on a calculator. When the Number Spirits' magic dust is rubbed on your lower arm, his final total mysteriously appears!

Materials

A calculator

Ground cinnamon

Paper and pencil

A glue stick

Preparation

Put a small amount of cinnamon or any dark spice in a small container. This is the Number Spirits' magic dust.

Write the number 1089 on the inside of your lower arm with a glue stick. The number should be invisible yet remain sticky.

Presentation	Example

1. Tell a friend to write any 3-digit number on a piece of paper without letting you see it. Tell him that the first digit must be *at least 2 greater* than the last digit.

831

2. Ask him to reverse the 3 digits and write this new number (138) below the first number. Have him subtract the two numbers on a calculator.

831
− 138
693

3. Tell him to reverse this difference and add this new number (396) to the calculator total.

693
+ 396
1089

4. Remind your friend that he was free to choose any 3-digit number, and then ask him for his final total. Then summon the Number Spirits. Ask them to make your friend's final total magically appear as you sprinkle their magic dust on your lower arm. Perform some hocus-pocus as you rub the magic dust around. Blow off the excess dust and, like magic, the number 1089 mysteriously appears!

The Secret
It does not matter which 3-digit number your friend starts with. If he does the arithmetic correctly, the final total will always be 1089!

Mathematical Oddity

Which sum is greater?

987654321		123456789
87654321		12345678
7654231		1234567
654321	or	123456
54321		12345
4321		1234
321		123
21		12
+ 1		+1

Believe it or not, they both equal 1,083,676,269!

SUPERMAN

You can prove to your friends that you have the power to see through solid objects by adding the *bottoms* of 5 dice!

Materials
5 dice

Presentation

1. Tell your friend that you are going to look through the dice and find the sum of the bottom numbers.

2. Throw 5 dice on the table.

3. Pretend that you can see through the dice all the way down to the bottom numbers. (What you are really doing is finding the sum of the top numbers.)

4. Announce the total of the 5 bottom numbers. (Just subtract the sum of the top numbers from 35.) Then *carefully* turn over the 5 dice and add the bottom numbers. Your friend won't believe her eyes!

Example

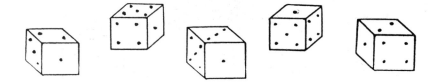

Sum of the top numbers = 13
35 − 13 = 22
So, the sum of the bottom numbers is 22!

The Secret

On any die, the sum of the top number and the bottom number is 7. So, if 5 dice are thrown, the total of all the top numbers and bottom numbers is:

5 x 7 = 35

Dice   Total

A Variation

Use a different number of dice and subtract the sum of the top numbers from a different number than 35. To find that number, just multiply the number of dice by 7.

YOUNG GENIUS

Your friends will think that you are ready for college when you add five large numbers in your head in just a few seconds!

Materials

Paper and pencil   A calculator

Preparation

Write this chart on a piece of paper

A	B	C	D	E
366	345	186	872	756
69	840	582	971	558
168	246	87	575	657
762	147	285	377	954
960	543	483	179	855
564	48	780	674	459

Presentation

While your back is turned, have a friend choose *one number* from each of the five columns and write them on a piece of paper. Tell her to add the five numbers using a calculator and write the answer underneath.

Example
762
246
483
674
+ 756
2,921

Finally, ask her to read off slowly the five numbers in any order so that you can add them in your head. You will have the answer in seconds!

How to Do It

As your friend reads the five numbers, just mentally add the *five last digits*.

$$2 + 6 + 3 + 4 + 6 = \underline{21}$$

Mentally subtract this sum from 50.

$$50 - 21 = \underline{29}$$

Put the second number in front of the first number to get the sum of all five numbers!

$$\underline{2, 9}\ \underline{21}!$$

PHOTOGRAPHIC MEMORY

Your friends are really impressed when you show them that you have memorized fifty different 6-digit and 7-digit numbers!

Materials

50 index cards

Paper and pencil

Preparation

Copy these numbers onto index cards—one to each card. The card number appears in italics.

1	5,055,055	*11*	5,167,303	*21*	5,279,651
2	6,066,280	*12*	6,178,538	*22*	6,280,886
3	7,077,415	*13*	7,189,763	*23*	7,291,011
4	8,088,640	*14*	8,190,998	*24*	8,202,246
5	9,099,875	*15*	9,101,123	*25*	9,213,471
6	112,358	*16*	224,606	*26*	336,954
7	1,123,583	*17*	1,235,831	*27*	1,347,189
8	2,134,718	*18*	2,246,066	*28*	2,358,314
9	3,145,943	*19*	3,257,291	*29*	3,369,549
10	4,156,178	*20*	4,268,426	*30*	4,370,774

31	5,381,909	*41*	5,493,257
32	6,392,134	*42*	6,404,482
33	7,303,369	*43*	7,415,617
34	8,314,594	*44*	8,426,842
35	9,325,729	*45*	9,437,077
36	448,202	*46*	550,550
37	1,459,437	*47*	1,561,785
38	2,460,662	*48*	2,572,910
39	3,471,897	*49*	3,583,145
40	4,482,022	*50*	4,594,370

Example

```
                              (35)
          9,325,729
```

Presentation

Shuffle the deck of index cards so that they are not in order, and then hand them to your friend. Tell her that there is a different number written on each card and that you have memorized all fifty numbers. Ask her to choose any card. When she tells you the card number, you are able to tell her which 6-digit or 7-digit number is on that card!

How To Do It

1. When your friend tells you the card number, mentally add 4 and then reverse your answer. The result is the first two digits.

Example: Card #35
35 + 4 = 39 and 39 reversed is 93.

The first two digits are 93.

2. To get the next digit, mentally add the first two digits together. If this sum is less than 10, write it down. If it is 10 or greater, only write down the number that is in the ones place.

$$9 + 3 = 1\underline{2} \qquad\qquad 93\underline{2}$$

3. Continue adding the last two digits to get the next one until you have written down all seven digits.

$3 + 2 = \underline{5}$	932<u>5</u>
$2 + 5 = \underline{7}$	9325<u>7</u>
$5 + 7 = 1\underline{2}$	93257<u>2</u>
$7 + 2 = \underline{9}$	932572<u>9</u>

Answer 9,325, 729

Exceptions

If your friend picks a card number that ends in 6, the number on that card has only six digits.

Example: Card #36
36 + 4 = 40 and 40 reversed is 04
The number is 0,448,202

(Don't say "Zero") ⬏

If your friend picks a card number from 1 to 5, mentally put a zero in the tens place before reversing your answer.

Example: Card #3
3 + 4 = 7 and *07* reversed is 70
The number is 7,077,415

A Variation
You can work the trick backwards. Tell your friend to give you the 6-digit or 7-digit number, and then you tell her the card number! When she tells you the number, reverse the first two digits and then subtract 4 to get the card number.

Example: The number is 1,235,831
12 reversed is 21 and 21 – 4 = 17
The card number is 17.

An Exception to This Variation
If your friend gives you a 6-digit number, mentally put the zero back in front, and then work the trick backwards.

Example: The number is 336,954
(0,336,954)
03 reversed is 30 and 30 – 4 = 26
The card number is 26.

BRAIN POWER

Your friends will think that you are an amazing number magician when you find the sum of ten numbers in just a few seconds!

Materials

A calculator   Paper and pencil

Preparation

Write the numbers 1–10 on a piece of paper, one under the other.

Presentation

1. Tell your friend to write any 1-digit number on the first line and a different 1-digit number on the second line.

Example
5 and 9

1. 5

2. Ask him to add these two numbers together and write their sum on the third line.

2. 9

3. 14

$$5 + 9 = 14$$

4. 23

3. Have him add line 2 and line 3 and write that sum on the fourth line.

5. 37

6. 60

$$9 + 14 = 23$$

7. 97

4. Tell him to continue adding in this manner until there is a list of ten numbers. Make sure that he is adding correctly. Each number in the list (except the first two) must be the sum of the two numbers above it.

8. 157

9. 254

10. 411

When your friend writes down the last number, quickly look at his list and pretend that you are adding all ten numbers in your head. Secretly write your answer on a piece of paper, fold it several times, and put it aside. Ask your friend to slowly add all ten numbers, using a calculator.

(Example: 1,067)

He will be amazed when you unfold the paper and your answer matches his final total!

How to Do It

When ten numbers are added in this manner,

The Final Total = the seventh number x 11!

So when you look at your friend's list, just look at the seventh number. Multiply that number by 11 on your piece of paper to get the final total.

Here is a quick way to multiply by 11:

Multiply the seventh number by 10.	(97 x 10)	970
Add the seventh number to that answer.	+	97
		1,067

Cross off your work so that your friend does not discover your secret. Make it look as if you have underlined your answer.

A Variation

Start with two 2-digit numbers and your friends will really be amazed!

MYSTERY POWDER

You and your friend write down five 4-digit numbers and add them using a calculator. When your secret mystery powder is rubbed over a piece of plastic, the correct answer magically appears!

Materials

A calculator
Paper and pencil
Glue stick
Ground cinnamon

Any piece of white plastic, such as the white lid from a plastic container

Preparation

Put a small amount of cinnamon or any dark spice into a small container. This is the mystery powder.

Write a number in the 20,000's on a piece of white plastic with a glue stick.

Example: 23,156

This is the Final Total. The number should be invisible yet remain sticky.

Figure out your *Key #*. First add 2 to the Final Total, and then cross off the first digit of your answer.

$$\begin{array}{r} 23{,}156 \\ +2 \\ \hline 23{,}158 \\ \text{\textit{Key \#}} \end{array}$$

Presentation

1. Ask a friend to write a 4-digit number on a piece of paper. The digits must be different and not form a pattern.

2. You write the *Key #*. ⟶

3. Tell your friend to write a different 4-digit number below your number.

4. You write a 4-digit number so that the sum of the first and fourth numbers = 9,999.

5. You write a 4-digit number so that the sum of the third and fifth numbers = 9,999.

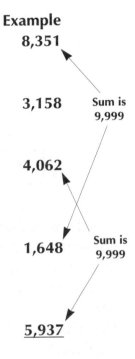

Example
8,351

3,158   Sum is 9,999

4,062

1,648   Sum is 9,999

5,937

Give your friend the piece of paper and ask him to add the five numbers using a calculator.

(23,156)

Sprinkle your mystery powder over the piece of white plastic, and then perform some hocus-pocus as you rub it around. Blow off the excess powder and—like magic—the Final Total mysteriously appears!

An Exception

Your friend writes a 9 for the first digit of the first number or the third number.

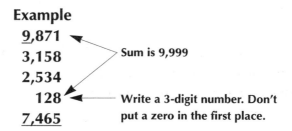

Example

9,871
3,158
2,534
 128
7,465

Sum is 9,999

Write a 3-digit number. Don't put a zero in the first place.

HAS ANYONE SEEN A GHOST?

This is a trick that you can do for a group of your friends or relatives. A prediction is put inside a shoe box and three random numbers are added using a calculator. When the shoe box is opened, your incorrect prediction has been mysteriously replaced by the correct answer!

Materials

A calculator
Shoe box
Marker
An index card
Pencil

A small spiral notebook that looks the same no matter which side is up.

Preparation

1. Write any 4-digit number on an index card with a marker, then cross it off. This is your prediction. Write a different 4-digit number (between 1000 and 2000) below the first number. Make it look like this number was written by a ghost. Put the card face down on the table.

2. Open the notebook to the middle and write down three 3-digit numbers. Make it look as if each 3-digit number was written by a different person. The sum of these numbers should equal the ghostly number on the piece of paper. Turn the notebook over and put it on the table with the blank side up.

```
526
847
470
```

Performance

Give the calculator to a friend who is in the back of the room and tell him that you will need his help later.

Show your friends that there is nothing inside the shoe box, and then put your prediction and the marker inside. Put the top on the shoe box and give it to your friend to hold.

Ask another friend to come up to the table and write a 3-digit number on the blank page in the notebook. Repeat this with two other friends. Don't let anyone turn over the notebook.

When the third number is written down, pick up the notebook and take it to your friend with the calculator. As you are walking over to your friend, *secretly turn over the notebook*. Show him the top page (*your three numbers*) and ask him to add the three numbers using the calculator. Close the notebook so that no one sees the other side. Tell your friend to announce the answer.

When your friend says the answer, look disappointed and admit that your prediction in the shoe box is incorrect. Make up a story about a ghost who is a friend of yours and explain that he will assist you with the trick. Ask your invisible friend to enter the shoe box, pick up the marker, cross off your prediction, and write the correct answer underneath. Repeat the answer one more time and then ask your friend to remove the piece of paper from the shoe box. To everyone's surprise, your ghostly assistant has saved the day by writing the correct answer below your prediction!

THE HUMAN COMPUTER

You can astound your friends by adding five 6-digit numbers in just a few seconds!

Materials

A calculator   Paper and pencil

Presentation

1. Ask a friend to write a 6-digit number on a piece of paper. The digits must be different and not form a pattern.

2. Tell her to write a second 6-digit number below her first number.

3. Ask her to write one more number. This third number is your *Key #*. ──────▶

4. You write a 6-digit number so that the sum of the first and the fourth numbers = 999,999.

5. You write a 6-digit number so that the sum of the second and fifth numbers = 999,999.

Example

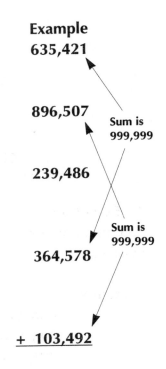

635,421

896,507   Sum is 999,999

239,486

Sum is 999,999

364,578

+ 103,492

Give your friend the piece of paper and ask her to add the five numbers using a calculator without letting you see the Final total—

(2,239,484).

When she hands you the paper, pretend that you are adding the five numbers in your head and quickly write down the Final Total!

How to Do It

When your friend hands you the paper, just look at the *Key #*, because the Final Total = 2,_____

(*Key #* minus 2).

Example:
Key # is 239,486
(*Key #* minus 2) = 239,484
The Final Total = 2,239,484

An Exception

Your friend writes a 9 for the first digit of the first number or the second number.

Example

$$956,231 \blacktriangleleft$$
$$623,178 \qquad \text{Sum is 999,999}$$
$$279,651$$
$$43,768 \blacktriangleleft \quad \text{Write a 5-digit number. Don't put a zero in the first place.}$$
$$\underline{376,821}$$

Variations

Seven 6-digit numbers:
The Final Total = 3,_____
(*Key #* minus 3)

Nine 6-digit numbers:
The Final Total = 4,_____
(*Key #* minus 4)

PSYCHIC PREDICTION

You are able to predict the sum of five 5-digit numbers before the trick begins! Also, when the digits of this sum are translated into letters, they spell your friend's name!

Materials

Paper and pencil   A calculator

Preparation

Write this chart on a piece of paper.

0	1	2	3	4	5	6	7	8	9
A	B	C	D	E	F	G	H	I	J
K	L	M	N	O	P	Q	R	S	T
U	V	W	X	Y	Z	.	,	!	?

Pick a friend who has three to six letters for a first or last name. (See *Variations* for more ideas.) The first letter must be a letter in the 2-column—C, M, or W.

Example: Cosby

Use the chart to translate your friend's name into a 6-digit number. This number is the Predicted Sum.

Cosby!
248,148

Figure out your *Key #*. Just add 2 to the Predicted Sum, and then cross off the first digit of your answer.

$$\begin{array}{r} 248,148 \\ +\qquad 2 \\ \hline \cancel{2}48,150 \end{array}$$

Presentation

Announce that you will write down the answer to a math problem before any numbers are given. Write the Predicted Sum on another piece of paper, fold it several times, and put it aside until later.

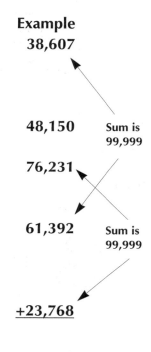

1. Ask your friend to write a 5-digit number on a piece of paper. The digits must be different and not form a pattern.

    Example
    38,607

2. You write down the *Key #*. ⟶   **48,150**   Sum is 99,999

3. Ask him to write another 5-digit number.   **76,231**

4. You write a 5-digit number so that the sum of the first and the fourth numbers = 99,999.   **61,392**   Sum is 99,999

5. You write a 5-digit number so that the sum of the third and the fifth numbers = 99,999.   **+23,768**

6. Ask him to add the five numbers on a calculator.   **248,148**

Finally, unfold your prediction and show your friend that it matches his answer! Then use the chart to translate his answer into letters and his name will magically appear!

    248,148
    COSBY!

Variations for Choosing a Name

Mr.C.!   MS.G.!   MRBLUM   MSROTH   MRS.J.

Other Variations

You could make words appear.

Example: MONDAY, MATH!!, MAGIC!, COLD!!, WEIGHT, etc.

Use your imagination! You could also rearrange the chart so that different letters appear in the 2-column. Then you could make many more names or words appear!

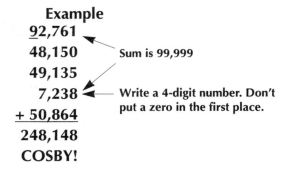

An Exception

Your friend writes a 9 for the first digit of the first number or the third number.

Example

9̲2,761
48,150   **Sum is 99,999**
49,135
   7,238 ◄— Write a 4-digit number. Don't
+ 50,864   put a zero in the first place.
248,148
COSBY!

CHAPTER TWO
CARD TRICKS

Card tricks are the most popular of all magic tricks. They can be performed anywhere and a regular deck of cards is all that is needed.

These card tricks are easy to learn and perform. No sleight of hand is required and, if you carefully follow the steps, they practically work themselves.

The tricks are organized from the easiest to the hardest, so choose those that are right for you. Even though the tricks are easy to learn, be sure to practice them by yourself first. When you have worked a trick through successfully two or three times, you are ready to perform it for others.

Never repeat a card trick for the same person or they might figure out the trick's secret. Perform a second trick instead, and everyone will have twice as much fun!

You will amaze your friends with your psychic powers when you look into the future and correctly predict the outcome of this card trick!

Materials

A deck of playing cards
An envelope

Paper and pencil

Preparation

Remove 9 red cards and 9 black cards from the deck.

Write "THERE WILL BE 2 MORE BLACK CARDS IN THE LONG ROW THAN RED CARDS IN THE SHORT ROW!" on a piece of paper and then seal it inside an envelope.

Presentation

1. Tell your friend that you have predicted the outcome of this trick and that you have sealed the prediction inside an envelope.

2. Hand him the 18 cards and ask him to shuffle them thoroughly.

3. Tell him to deal the cards face up in 2 rows in any order that he chooses. The first row should have 7 cards and the second row should have 11 cards.

4. Finally, remind your friend that he was free to choose the cards that were dealt into each row. Then open up your prediction and show him that it is correct. Your friend will think that you possess supernatural powers!

The Secret
The difference in the lengths of the rows determines the prediction. 11 – 7 = 4 and half of 4 is 2. So there will always be 2 more blacks in the long row than reds in the short row. Also, there will be 2 more reds in the long row than blacks in the short row.

A Variation
Start with 15 red cards and 15 black cards. Put 11 cards in the short row and 19 cards in the long row and see how your prediction changes.

There will be four more black cards in the long row than red cards in the short row.

Riddle Me

Why is it dangerous to do math in the jungle?

If you multiply 4 and 2 you will get 8 (ate)!

TREE OF CLUBS

You secretly predict which card will be chosen from the deck. It looks as if the "Number Spirits" have played a trick on you when your friend's chosen card doesn't match your prediction—or does it?

Materials

An envelope   Tape
A deck of playing cards with a Joker

Preparation

Photocopy the card on this page, cut around it and then tape or laminate it over the Joker. Seal this card inside an envelope.

Put the 3 of Clubs on top of the deck and put the 8 of Clubs in the ninth position down from the top of the deck.

Presentation

1. Tell your friend that he will randomly select a card from the deck and that the card in the envelope will match his selected card.

2. Ask him for a number *between* 10 and 20. (*Caution:* Between does not include 10 or 20.)

Example

17

3. Deal that many cards into a small pile, one card at a time.

4. Ask your friend to find the sum of the digits of his number.

17 → 1 + 7 = 8

5. Return that many cards to the top of the big pile, one card at a time.

Return 8 cards

6. Put the rest of the small pile on top of the big pile.

7. Pretend to perform some supernatural hocus-pocus as you ask the "Number Spirits" for a sign that will tell your friend how many cards he should count down in the deck. Pretend that they tell you to turn over the top card. It will be the 8 of Clubs. This sign means that your friend should count down 8 cards in the deck and turn over the eighth card. It will be the 3 of Clubs.

8. Finally, remind your friend that he was free to choose any number. Then open up the envelope and pull out the Tree of Clubs. Act surprised and upset, and then blame the "Number Spirits" for switching cards and playing a mean trick on you. But wait! The trick worked after all!

The 3 of Clubs = The Tree of Clubs

The Secret
This trick uses a mathematical procedure called casting out nines. Any number between 10 and 20 minus the sum of its digits always equals 9.

LAST CARD

Your friend will be mystified when you correctly predict the number of cards that she secretly removes from the deck!

Materials
A deck of playing cards with a Joker
Tape

Preparation
Photocopy the card on this page, cut the card out and then tape or laminate it over one of the Jokers.

Put this card in the twenty-first position down from the top of the deck.

Presentation

1. Hand your friend the deck of cards. When your back is turned, ask her to remove from 1 to 15 cards from the *top* of the deck. Tell her to hide them in her hand.

2. Turn around and ask her to concentrate on the number of cards that she removed. Pretend that you are reading her mind as you *quietly* deal out 20 cards, one at a time, face down on the table. Put this pack of 20 cards in your hand and then set the rest of the deck aside.

3. Tell your friend to turn her cards over one at a time on the table. Every time she turns over a card, turn over the top card from your pack and put it face up on top of hers.

4. Continue turning over cards until hers are all gone. When she runs out of cards your next card will say, "THAT WAS YOUR LAST CARD!" It works every time, no matter how many cards your friend removes!

The Secret

When you count out 20 cards, their order is reversed. This puts the "THAT WAS YOUR LAST CARD!" card a certain number down from the top. That number will always equal the number of cards that your friend removes.

Favorite Number

Pick any number from 1 to 9. See what happens when you multiply that number by 259 and by 429. After you get the answer, clear your calculator. Then multiply 259 x 429 and you will see why it works.

YOUR SELECTED CARD IS...

Your friend secretly chooses a card from a deck of cards. When a magical phrase is spelled out, your friend's chosen card suddenly appears!

Materials
A complete deck of 52 playing cards with no Jokers

Presentation

1. Hand your friend a deck of cards, and tell her to shuffle them thoroughly.

2. Ask her to try to cut the deck into two equal packs. (It does not matter if the packs are equal, but each one should have between 20 and 30 cards.)

Example: 28 cards and 24 cards

3. Tell her to choose either pack and put the other pack aside until later.

4. Ask her to count the cards in her pack to see how close she got to 26. (If her pack does not have between 20 and 30 cards, ask her to start over and cut the entire deck again.)

5. Suppose your friend chooses the pack of 28 cards. Ask her to find the sum of the digits of that number.

28   2 + 8 = 10

6. Tell her to deal that many cards into a small pile, and then memorize the top card of that pile. Have her put the rest of her pack on top of this small pile.

7. Ask her to put her pack on top of the other pack that she did not choose, and then hand you the entire deck of cards.

8. Explain to your friend that you are going to spell out a magical phrase that will help you find her card. Deal cards from the top of the deck, one at a time, as you spell this phrase out loud: "Y-O-U-R S-E-L-E-C-T-E-D C-A-R-D I-S." Turn over 1 card for each letter of the phrase. The *next card* is your friend's selected card!

The Secret

This trick uses a mathematical procedure called casting out nines. Any number between 20 and 30 minus the sum of its digits always equals 18. This equals the number of letters in the magical phrase.

Riddle Me

What did the acorn say when it grew up?

Gee, I'm a tree (geometry)!

COME FORTH

Your friend will be astonished when you command his chosen card to come forth, and it rises up out of the deck!

Materials
A complete deck of 52 playing cards with no Jokers

Presentation

1. Have your friend shuffle the cards as many times as he wants. When he is finished, tell him to memorize the *bottom card*. **Example: Ace of Hearts**

2. Ask him to put the deck on the table and turn over the top 3 cards.

3. Tell your friend to deal cards face down below each of these 3 cards. He should start with the number on the face-up card (Aces = 1, Jacks = 11, Queens = 12, and Kings = 13), and then keep dealing cards until he gets to 15. For example, if the face-up card is a 9, he would deal 6 more cards to get to 15.

Example

| 6 more cards | 3 more cards | 5 more cards |

4. Ask him to keep the 3 face-up cards on the table, and then put all the face-down cards on the *bottom* of the deck.

5. Have him find the sum of the 3 face-up cards (**9 + Q + 10 = 31**) Tell him to deal out that many cards, and then put them on the *bottom* of the deck.

$$(12)$$

6. Explain that you have supernatural powers and that you can force any card to come out of the deck on your command. Ask your friend for the name of his card so that you can command it to come out. He says, "It was the Ace of Hearts."

7. Pretend to do some hocus-pocus as you say, "Ace of Hearts, come forth!" Repeat your command, and then look pleased with the result.

8. Your friend, of course, won't see anything happen, but you insist that his card did come forth. Turn over cards off the top of the deck one at a time and say, "Here's the first card, here's the second, here's the third, and the Ace of Hearts comes FOURTH!" Turn over the fourth card and it will be your friend's card!

The Secret
Each face-up card + counting up to 15 + the value of the card = 16. So 16 x 3 face-up cards = 48. Then 48 + 4 (come fourth) = 52 cards in the deck.

WIZARD OF ODDS

You and your friend each select a card from your own deck of cards. The probability that you will select identical cards is 1 out of 2,704. But for some magical reason, you are able to beat the odds every time!

Materials
2 decks of playing cards without Jokers

Presentation

1. Have two decks of cards on the table, one for you and one for your friend.

2. Tell your friend to do exactly what you do. If you shuffle your deck, she should shuffle her deck. If you turn your deck around, she should turn her deck around, and so on.

3. This part of the trick is nothing more than a little hocus-pocus. Shuffle, double cut, turn, shuffle again, and triple cut your deck. Make sure that your friend does the same with her deck.

4. Flip your deck over, and then turn your deck clockwise and then counterclockwise 2 or 3 times. She should be doing the same with her deck. While you are doing this, it is very important that you *memorize your friend's bottom card*—this is your *key card*.

5. Turn your deck face down once again. Then pick out a card from near the center of your deck. Pretend that you are memorizing your card (but you only need to remember the key card on the bottom of your friend's deck) and then place it *on top of your deck*. Your friend does the same with her deck.

6. Each of you should cut your deck in half once so that the chosen cards are lost in the middle of their decks. This puts the key card on top of her chosen card.

7. Finally, exchange decks with your friend. Tell your friend to find her card and that you will find yours. Look through the cards until you see the key card. Your friend's chosen card will be the card *to the right* of the key card. Pretend that her chosen card is yours, remove it, and place it face down on the table. Your friend does the same with her card.

8. Explain to your friend that the probability of choosing identical cards is very small—1 out of 2,704 ($1/52 \times 1/52 = 1/2,704$). Your friend won't believe her eyes when you flip the cards over and they are identical!

ROYAL HEADACHE

Your friends will be amazed when you correctly predict which card will be chosen from the 20 cards on the table!

Materials

Paper and pencil   An envelope
A deck of playing cards

Preparation

Use 20 cards to make a figure 9 on the table. The values of the cards are not important but be sure that the suits are in the same order as shown in the diagram. Put the King of Hearts where the x is in the diagram.

Write "YOU WILL CHOSE THE KING WHO HAS A SWORD STUCK IN HIS LEFT EAR!" on a piece of paper and seal it inside an envelope.

Presentation

1. Tell your friend that you have predicted which card he will choose and that you have sealed the prediction inside an envelope.

2. Ask him to think of any counting number *between* 5 and 20. (*Caution:* This number must be greater than 5.) Tell him to start counting from the end of the 9's tail. (The first card is counted as number 1.) He should continue counting up and around counterclockwise until he gets to his number. Tell him to keep his finger on that card.

3. Remove the 5 cards from the 9's tail and put them aside, leaving only a circle.

4. Now ask your friend to count in the opposite direction—clockwise—around the circle until he gets to his number. (The card that his finger is on is counted as number 1.)

5. Remove the 5 Club cards from the circle.

6. Tell him to count 6 cards in either direction. (Again, the card that his finger is on is number 1.) No matter which direction he goes, he will end up on the King of Hearts!

7. Finally, remind your friend that he was free to choose any number. Then open up your prediction and show him what you wrote. He won't believe his eyes. He will think that you have E.S.P.!

The Secret
When you count one way around a circle and then count that same number in the opposite direction, you always end up in the same place. The 9's tail helps hide this secret.

IDENTICAL TWINS

Your friend randomly chooses any card on the table. He will be amazed when your prediction is opened and it matches his card!

Materials

Two decks of cards
An envelope

A coin

Preparation

Secretly seal an Ace of Hearts from a second deck in an envelope.

Place nine cards on the table in front of your friend. Be sure that they are in the *same order* as shown in the diagram.

Sit across the table from your friend, and put something between the two of you so that you cannot see the cards.

Presentation

Tell your friend that you have predicted which card he will choose and that you have sealed the prediction inside an envelope.

Ask him to place the coin on top of any of the four Queens. Tell him that he will be free to move that coin wherever he wants, but at the end of the trick, it will be sitting on your predicted card.

Explain that he can move the coin horizontally, vertically, forward or backwards, but *never diagonally*. Also, he cannot skip over cards. Make sure that the coin is on any Queen and then tell your friend to:

1. Move 6 times and then remove the Jack of Diamonds.

2. Move 3 times and then remove the Queen of Spades.

3. Move 2 times and then remove the Queen of Clubs.

4. Move 3 times and then remove the King of Diamonds and the Ace of Spades.

5. Move 2 times and then remove the King of Clubs.

6. Move 1 time and then remove the two red Queens.

If your friend followed your instructions, the coin will be on the Ace of Hearts!

Remind your friend that he was free to move the coin wherever he wanted. Then open your prediction and show him that the two cards are identical!

The Secret

There are only certain cards that you can land on when you move an even number or an odd number of times. Those cards that you *cannot* land on are removed. In the end, every card is removed except the Ace of Hearts.

SWITCHEROO

A deck of cards is divided into two piles. Your friend secretly takes a card from each pile and places it in the opposite pile. Even though each pile is thoroughly shuffled, you are able to find your friend's two cards!

Materials
A deck of playing cards without Jokers

Preparation
Put all the even cards in one pile (2, 4 ,6, 8, 10, Queen) and all the odd cards in another pile (Ace, 3, 5, 7, 9, Jack, King). Shuffle each pile so that it is well mixed.

Presentation

1. Have your friend shuffle each pile separately without looking at the cards. Spread both piles face down on the table.

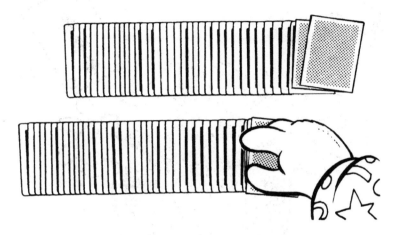

2. Tell her to choose one card from the group at the top, look at it, and place it in the group on the bottom. Then have her choose a different card from the group at the bottom, look at it, and place it in the group on the top.

3. Have her shuffle each pile, put one pile on top of the other, and hand you the deck of cards. Within seconds, you are able to reveal her two cards!

How to Do It
The odd card that is chosen will be surrounded by even cards, and the even card that is chosen will be surrounded by odd cards.

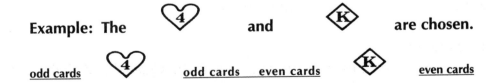

ELEVEN IN A ROW

Eleven cards are placed face down in a straight row on a table. After you leave the room, your friend moves some of the cards. When you return, you are able to tell how many cards were moved even though the row looks exactly the way it did when you left the room!

Materials
A deck of playing cards

Preparation
Take the following eleven cards out of the deck: Any Joker and any cards from Ace through 10. Place them face down on a table in order in a straight row.

Left | J OKER | A | 2 | 3 | 4 | 5 | 6 | 7 | 8 | 9 | 10 | Right

(All cards should be face down)

Presentation

1. Tell your friend that when you leave the room, he should move some cards from the left end of the row to the right end of the row, *one card at a time*. He may move any number of cards from 0 to 10.

2. Before you leave the room, move some of the cards yourself to show him how they should be moved. You are really doing this to get your *Key #*.

Example
You move 3 cards
(This is your *Key #*—remember it!)

Left | J OKER | A | 2 | 3 | 4 | 5 | 6 | 7 | 8 | 9 | 10 | J OKER | A | 2 | Right

3. Leave the room and have your friend move some of the cards.

Example
He moves 5 cards

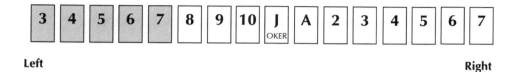

Left   **Right**

4. When you return, perform some hocus-pocus and pretend that the cards are speaking to you. Tell your friend that the cards will reveal the number of cards that he moved. Remember your *Key #* and count over that many cards from the *right end* of the row. Turn this card over and the number on that card will tell you how many cards your friend moved! (The Joker = 0 and Ace = 1.)

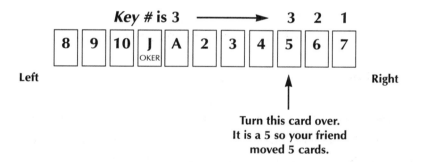

Key # is 3 ⟶   3   2   1

8 9 10 J OKER A 2 3 4 5 6 7

Left   **Right**

Turn this card over.
It is a 5 so your friend
moved 5 cards.

A Variation
Use a different *Key #* each time you perform the trick.

CRYSTAL BALL

Your calculator becomes your magical crystal ball when it mystically reveals a 2-digit number that is concealed inside a deck of cards!

Materials

A deck of playing cards   A calculator

Preparation

Remove all the 10s and face cards from a deck of cards so that your deck has only Aces through 9s.

Presentation

Ask your friend to shuffle the deck, remove two cards without looking at them, and place them face down on the table. The rest of the deck can be set aside.

Tell him to secretly look at either card and memorize its number (Ace = 1). Its suit is not important. You look at the other card, and then both cards are returned face down on the table. Put your card one inch to the right of your friend's card. Explain that the two cards represent a 2-digit number and that the calculator will be your crystal ball that will reveal that number.

Hand your friend the calculator and have him:

1. Enter the number of his card.   **9**

2. Multiply that number by 2.   **9 x 2 = 18**

3. Add 2 to that result.   **18 + 2 = 20**

4. Multiply that answer by 5.   **20 x 5 = 100**

5. Subtract the Magic Number.
The Magic Number is
   10 minus your card number.
    (10 – 3 = 7)   **100 – 7 = 93**

Finally, have your friend turn over the two cards on the table. The 2-digit number that is formed by the two cards will match the number that appears in the crystal ball!

INVISIBLE DECK

After your friend picks a card from your "invisible deck" and works a few problems on a calculator, you are able to announce the name of her invisible card!

Materials

A calculator   Paper and pencil

Preparation

Write these charts on a piece of paper.

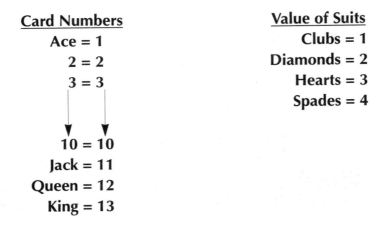

Presentation

Pretend to have an invisible deck in your hands. Shuffle it thoroughly, and then ask a friend to pick a card from your "deck." Tell her to write the name of her card on a piece of paper.

Example: 7 of Hearts

Hand her the calculator and ask her to:

1. Enter the card's number.   7

2. Add the number that is one more than this number.
(7 + 1 = 8)   7 + 8 = 15

3. Multiply that result by 5.   15 x 5 = 75

4. Add the value of the suit to that answer.
(Hearts = 3)   75 + 3 = 78

5. Add 637 to that result.   78 + 637 = 715

Then, tell your friend to hand you the calculator with the final total. Just subtract 642 and her card will magically appear!

$$\begin{array}{r} 7\,1\,5 \\ -\,6\,4\,2 \\ \hline 7\ 3 \end{array}$$

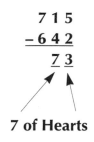

7 of Hearts

An Exception
When your subtract 642 and get three digits, the first two digits are the card's number.

Example: 12 4

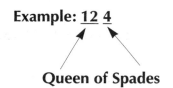

Queen of Spades

A Variation
Perform the trick with two or more friends at the same time. Before you announce their cards, pretend to +, −, x, and ÷ their totals so that they will think that their answers are somehow related to each other.

ABRACADABRA

You friend mentally chooses a card from a pile of 21 cards. When the magic word "ABRACADABRA" is spelled out, your friend's chosen card suddenly appears!

Materials
A deck of playing cards

Presentation

1. Shuffle the deck, count out 21 cards, and set the rest of the deck aside.

2. Deal out three piles of seven cards each, face down on the table. Deal the cards from left to right, one pile at a time, as if you were dealing to three players in a card game. There is no need for you ever to see the faces of any of the cards.

3. Ask your friend to choose one of the piles. Take the pile that he chose in your hand, fan out the cards towards him, and ask him to mentally select any card.

4. Put the pile that he chose between the other two piles so that you again have a pack of 21 cards in your hand.

5. Once more, deal out three piles of seven cards each, face down on the table. Taking up one pile at a time, fan out the cards towards your friend and ask him which pile has his chosen card. Again, put the pile that has his chosen card between the other two piles so that you have a pack of 21 cards in your hand.

6. Repeat Step 5 one more time.

7. Tell your friend that you are going to say the magic word "ABRA-CADABRA" and his chosen card will magically appear. Slowly spell "ABRACADABRA," turning over one card for each letter. The last card that you turn over will be your friend's chosen card!!

FOUR ACE BAFFLER

Three cards are randomly removed from the deck and they are all Aces! Then the "number spirits" are summoned and the fourth Ace mysteriously appears!

Materials

A deck of playing cards

Preparation

Put an 8 card in the eighth position down from the top of the deck and put the four Aces in the ninth, tenth, eleventh and twelfth positions.

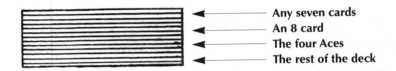

Any seven cards
An 8 card
The four Aces
The rest of the deck

Presentation

1. Ask a friend for a number *between* 10 and 20. (*Caution:* 10 will work, but 20 will not.)

Example
13

2. Deal that number of cards into a small pile one card at a time. Place the rest of the deck next to the small pile.

◄——— **13 cards**

3. Ask your friend to add the digits of that number.

13 ——► 1 + 3 = 4

4. Return that many cards to the top of the big pile one card at a time.

Return four cards

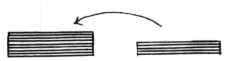

5. The top card of the small pile will be an Ace! Turn this card face up and show your friend.

6. Set the Ace aside and put the small pile on top of the big pile.

7. Repeat the six steps with two *different* numbers between 10 and 20 to remove two more Aces.

Finally, pretend to do some supernatural hocus-pocus as you ask the "number spirits" for a sign to help you find the last Ace. Pretend that they tell you to turn over the top card. It will be an 8. Count down eight more cards and the eighth card will the the fourth Ace!

MYSTERIOUS FORCE

You secretly predict which card will be chosen from the deck, and then the "number spirits" mysteriously force your friend to choose that card!

Materials

A deck of playing cards, complete with 52 cards plus two Jokers

Paper and pencil
A calculator, if needed

Presentation

1. Have your friend shuffle the cards as many times as she wants.

2. When she hands you the cards, say that you forgot to take out the Jokers. Turn the cards over, remove the Jokers, and sneak a peek at the bottom card. This is the "predicted card."

3. Secretly write the name of the "predicted card" on a piece of paper, fold it several times, and put it aside until later.

4. Tell your friend that a supernatural mathematical power will force her to choose your predicted card.

5. Deal out twelve cards face down from the top of the deck and spread them out on the table. Ask your friend to turn any four of these cards face up.

6. Put the other eight cards on the *bottom* of the deck.

Example

7. Hand your friend the deck and tell her to deal cards face down below each of these cards. She should start with the number on the face up card (All face cards = 10 and Aces = 1), and then keep dealing cards until she gets to 10. For example, if the face-up card is a 6, she would deal four more cards to get to 10.

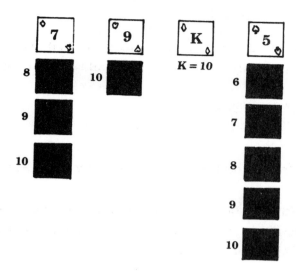

8. Tell her to keep the four face up cards on the table and put all the face down cards on the *bottom* of the deck.

9. Ask her to find the sum of the four cards:

$$(10)$$
$$7 + 9 + K + 5 = 31$$

10. Have her count down that many cards in the deck and turn the last card face up. (Turn card #31 face up.) This is her chosen card. Finally, unfold your prediction and show your friend that it matches her chosen card!

A Variation

If your deck of cards has no Jokers, sneak a peak at the bottom card after your friend hands you the deck.

POCKET PUZZLER

Your friend removes four cards from the deck and secretly puts one of them in her pocket. After performing some number magic on a calculator, you are able to reveal the card that is hidden in your friend's pocket!

Materials

A deck of playing cards   A calculator
Paper and pencil

Presentation

1. Ask your friend to write any 4-digit number on a piece of paper without letting you see it. Tell her that all four digits must be different.

Example
8756

2. Tell her to add the four digits together and write the sum below the first number. **(8 + 7 + 5 + 6 = 26)**

– 26

3. Have her subtract the two numbers, using a calculator.

8730

4. Hand her the deck of cards and ask her to secretly remove four cards that have the same numbers as the four digits. (Ace = 1 and 0 = King) Also, tell her that each card must be of a different suit.

Example
8 = 8 of Hearts
7 = 7 of Clubs
3 = 3 of Diamonds
0 = King of Spades

5. Tell her to put one of the cards *that is not a King* in her pocket, and then hand you the other three cards.

Example: She puts the 3 of Diamonds in her pocket and hands you the 8 of Hearts, the 7 of Clubs, and the King of Spades.

6. Mentally add the values of these three cards.

8 + 7 + 0 = 15

If your answer has more than one digit, add the digits together until there is only one digit.

15 → 1 + 5 = 6

7. Mentally subtract this number from 9, and the value of the card that is in your friend's pocket will magically appear.

9 − 6 = 3

The card that is in your friend's pocket is a 3 and since the only suit that is missing is Diamonds, your friend's card is:

The 3 of Diamonds!

An Exception
When you mentally subtract from 9 and get 0, your friend's card is a 9—not a King.

CHAPTER THREE
CALCULATOR
CONJURING

Did you know that your calculator is a talented magician? If you enter the correct numbers, it will perform many magic tricks for you!

All of the magic tricks in this chapter are performed on an ordinary calculator. The tricks are organized from the easiest to the hardest, so choose those that are right for you. They are easy to learn and perform but you still need to practice them by yourself first. You should work a trick through successfully two or three times before you perform it for others.

You have to be very careful, however, and make sure you push the right buttons or the trick will not work. Perform each trick *slowly* so that you don't make careless errors.

Finally, remember that magicians never reveal their secrets. If someone asks you how you did a trick, just say, "Very carefully!" If they still question you, tell them to ask your calculator!

SEVEN-UP

You have the luckiest calculator in the world. No matter which number your friend enters, it is magically transformed into the lucky number 7!

Materials
A calculator

Presentation
Hand your friend the calculator and have her:

	Example
1. Enter any number that is easy to remember. (This number must be less than 8 digits.)	**123**
2. Double that number.	**123 x 2 = 246**
3. Subtract 16 from that answer.	**246 – 16 = 230**
4. Multiply that result by 4.	**230 x 4 = 920**
5. Divide that total by 8.	**920 ÷ 8 = 115**
6. Add 15 to that answer.	**115 + 15 = 130**
7. Subtract her original number from that result.	**130 – 123 = 7**

This trick can be repeated several times with the same friend. No matter which number she starts with, the final answer will always end up "lucky"!

The Secret

All of the tricks in this chapter were written using a branch of mathematics called algebra. In this trick, if all of the operations are carefully performed, your friend's original number is eliminated. Adding 15 in Step 6 guarantees that the final total will always be 7.

A Variation

Experiment by adding a different number in Step 6 and the final total will be a different number.

PAIR-A-DICE

Your friend rolls 2 dice when you are not looking. After he works a few problems on a calculator, you are able to reveal the two top numbers on the dice!

Materials
2 dice
Paper and pencil
A calculator

Presentation

When your back is turned,
have a friend:

1. Roll two dice.

2. Multiply the top number
on the first die by 5, using a
calculator or paper and pencil.

$$\underline{2} \times 5 = 10$$

3. Add 12 to that answer.

$$10 + 2 = 22$$

4. Double that total.

$$22 \times 2 = 44$$

5. Add that result to the top
number on the second die.

$$44 + \underline{6} = 50$$

6. Add 15 to that answer.

$$50 + 15 = 65$$

Finally, ask your friend for his final total. Just subtract 39 and the top numbers on the dice will magically appear!

$$
\begin{array}{r}
6\,5 \\
-\,3\,9 \\
\hline
\underline{2}\ \underline{6} \\
\end{array}
$$

1st   2nd
die   die

The Secret

Multiplying by 5 and then doubling is just like multiplying by 10. This puts the number on the first die in the tens place. Adding the number on the second die puts that number in the ones place. Every other operation is mathematical hocus-pocus and adds an extra 39 to the total. Subtracting this 39 reveals the two top numbers on the dice.

SPECIAL FRIEND

Your friend will think that you possess supernatural powers when you correctly reveal the name that she has chosen from a list of her friends!

Materials

A calculator   Paper and pencil

Presentation

Ask your friend to make a list of at least five of her friends' names. Tell her to number each name.

Then ask her to:

1. Write the number of a "special" friend on a piece of paper without showing you.	**Example Friend #8**
2. Multiply that number by 5.	**8 x 5 = 40**
3. Add 5 to that result.	**40 + 5 = 45**
4. Double that answer.	**45 x 2 = 90**
5. Add 45 to that total.	**90 + 45 = 135**

6. Cross off the last digit of that answer.   13~~X~~

7. Add 44 to that result.   13 + 44 = 57

Finally, ask your friend for her final total. Just subtract 49 and the number of her special friend will magically appear!

$$\begin{array}{r} 57 \\ -\ 49 \\ \hline \end{array}$$

Friend # 8 ➜   **8**

The Secret

If all of the operations are carefully performed, the final total will always be 49 more than the special friend's number. Subtracting 49 reveals that number.

BIRTHDAY SURPRISE

You will be able to divulge anyone's age and the year they were born by simply performing some number magic on a calculator!

Materials

A calculator

Presentation

Hand someone a calculator and ask her to:

	Example
	Year Born: 1955
	Age: 39

1. Enter the year that she was born, without letting you see it.

$$1955$$

2. Multiply that year by 2.

$$1955 \times 2 = 3{,}910$$

3. Add the number of months in a year.

$$3{,}910 + 12 = 3{,}922$$

4. Multiply that total by 50.

$$3{,}922 \times 50 = 196{,}100$$

5. Add her age to that result.

$$196{,}100 + 39 = 196{,}139$$

6. Add the number of days in a year.

$$196{,}139 + 365 = 196{,}504$$

Finally, tell her to hand you the calculator with the final total. Just subtract 965, and the year that she was born and her age will magically appear!

$$
\begin{array}{r}
196504 \\
-\quad 965 \\
\hline
\underline{1955}\ \underline{39} \\
\end{array}
$$

Year   Age
Born

Exceptions

If the person's age is less than 10, the tens place will be 0.

Example: 198905 = <u>1989</u> <u>05</u>, so age = 5

If it happens to be a leap year, add 366 in Step 6 and then subtract 966 from the final total.

The Secret

Multiplying the year by 2 and then by 50 is just like multiplying by 100. This moves the year over two and to the left of the hundreds place. Adding the age puts that number in the last two places. Every other operation is mathematical hocus-pocus and adds an extra 965 to the total. Subtracting this 965 reveals the year born and age.

LAST LAUGH

A card from a second deck is sealed in an envelope. You predict that this card will match your friend's chosen card. At the end it appears as though you have made a mistake, but you always end up getting the last laugh!

Materials

A calculator   2 decks of playing cards
An envelope

Preparation

Tear off the top half of the 10 of Diamonds from an old deck of cards so that only five of the ten diamonds are showing. Seal this card in an envelope.

Put the 5 of Diamonds in the eleventh position down from the top of the deck.

Presentation

Tell your friend that he will randomly select a card from the deck and that the card in the envelope will match his selected card.

Hand your friend the calculator and have him:

1. Enter his address or any other counting number that is easy to remember. (This number must be less than 7 digits.)	**Example**
	41
2. Multiply that number by 100.	**41 x 100 = 4100**
3. Subtract his original number from that answer.	**4100 – 41 = 4059**

4. Divide that total by his original number.   **4059 ÷ 41 = 99**

5. Divide that result by 9.   **99 ÷ 9 = 11**

Finally, remind your friend that he was free to choose any number. Then ask him for his final total. Have him count down that many cards in the deck and turn over the eleventh card, the 5 of Diamonds.

Open up the envelope and slowly slide out the 10 of Diamonds, being careful not to show the missing bottom. Your friend will think that you have made a mistake. Then slide the card all the way out and have him count the diamonds. Your prediction is correct after all because there are only 5 diamonds!

The Secret
Multiplying any counting number by 100, subtracting the number, and then dividing by the number always equals 99. Finally, dividing by 9 results in 11 for the final total.

DOUBLE TROUBLE

Pick any 1-, 2-, or 3-digit number. See what happens when you multiply that number by 7, then by 11, and finally by 13. After you get the answer, clear your calculator. Then multiply 7 x 11 x 13 and you will see why it works.

ORANGE ELEPHANT

Your friends are amazed with your mystical powers when you look into the future and reveal their deepest thoughts.

Materials

A calculator   Paper and pencil
An envelope

Preparation

Write "AN ORANGE ELEPHANT FROM FLORIDA" on a piece of paper and seal it inside an envelope.

Presentation

Tell your friend that you have predicted the outcome of this trick and that you have sealed the prediction inside an envelope.
   Then hand her the calculator and ask her to:

	Example
1. Enter any number that is easy to remember in the calculator without letting you see it. (This number must be less than 8 digits.)	99

2. Multiply that number by 4.   **99 x 4 = 396**

3. Add 25 to that result.   **396 + 25 = 421**

4. Double that answer.   **421 x 2 = 842**

5. Subtract 2 from that total.   **842 – 2 = 840**

6. Divide that result by 8.   **840 ÷ 8 = 105**

7. Subtract her original number
from that total.   **105 – 99 = 6**

Ask your friend to write her
final result on a piece of paper.   **6**

Tell her to number the letters of
the alphabet (A = 1, B = 2, C = 3, etc.)
and write down the letter that equals
her number.   **6 = F**

Ask her to write down the name of a
U.S. state that starts with that letter.   **F = Florida**

Tell her to look at the third letter
of that state and write down a basic
color that starts with that letter.   **o = orange**

Ask her to look at the last letter of that
color and write down the name of a very
large animal that starts with that letter.   **e = elephant**

Finally, open up your prediction. Unbelievably, it should match her 3
answers.

An **orange elephant** from **Florida!**

The Secret
If all of the operations are carefully performed, your friend's original number is eliminated and the final total will always be 6.

A Variation
Instead of making a prediction, have your friend concentrate on her three answers and then pretend that you are reading her mind.

CONCEALED COIN

This is a trick you can do for a group of your friends or relatives. When your back is turned, someone hides a coin in one of their hands. After you work some number magic, you are able to disclose who has the coin and which hand it is hiding in!

Materials

A calculator   A coin
Paper and pencil

Presentation

Pick one of your friends to be your assistant, and then number the rest of your friends starting with number 1. While your back is turned, have your assistant hide a coin in someone's hand. Tell him to write down that person's number and the hand that is hiding the coin. Tell everyone else to make fists with their hands.

Hand your assistant the calculator and have him:	**Example** **Friend #4** **Right Hand**
1. Enter the number of the person who has the coin.	**4**
2. Multiply that number by 5.	**4 x 5 = 20**
3. Add 13 to that answer.	**20 + 13 = 33**
4. Multiply that result by 4.	**33 x 4 = 132**
5. Add 88 to that total.	**132 + 88 = 220**
6. Divide that answer by 2.	**220 ÷ 2 = 110**
7. Add 4 if the coin is hidden in the left hand. Add 5 if the coin is hidden in the right hand.	**110 + 5 = 115**
8. Add 50 to that result.	**115 + 50 = 165**

Finally, ask your assistant to hand you the calculator with the final total. Just subtract 123 and you will be able to find that coin!

$$
\begin{array}{r}
1\ 6\ 5 \\
-\ 1\ 2\ 3 \\
\hline
4\ 2
\end{array}
$$

Person #4 ⟶ **4 2** ◀ Hand
1 = left
2 = right

An Exception

When you subtract 123 and get three digits, the first two digits are the number of the person.

$$
\begin{array}{r}
2\ 7\ 4 \\
-\ 1\ 2\ 3 \\
\hline
1\ 5\ 1
\end{array}
$$

Person #15 ⟶ **1 5 1** ◀ Left Hand

The Secret

Multiplying the person's number by 5 and 4 and then dividing by 2 is just like multiplying by 10. This moves the person's number over two and to the left of the tens place. Adding the hand puts that number in the ones place. Every other addition is mathematical hocus-pocus and adds an extra 123 to the total. Subtracting this 123 reveals the person's number and the correct hand.

Riddle Me

Why did the math book go on a diet?

It had a lot of fractions to reduce!

BEWITCHED

Someone has placed an evil spell on your calculator. No matter which number your friend enters, it is ghoulishly transformed into the unlucky number 13!

Materials
A calculator

Presentation
Have a friend:

	Example
1. Enter in the calculator any number that is easy to remember—address, age, phone number, etc. (This number must be less than 8 digits.)	**77**
2. Double that number.	**77 x 2 = 154**
3. Add 15 to that answer.	**154 + 15 = 169**
4. Triple that result.	**169 x 3 = 507**
5. Add 33 to that total.	**507 + 33 = 540**
6. Divide that answer by 6.	**540 ÷ 6 = 90**
7. Subtract her original number.	**90 – 77 = 13**

This is a trick that can be repeated several times with the same friend. The final answer always ends up "unlucky"!

GIVE ME 5!

With your X-ray vision, you are able to see through the back of a calculator and reveal the number that appears in the display!

Materials
A calculator

Presentation
Have a friend:

	Example
1. Enter any number that is easy to remember in the calculator without letting you see it. (This number must be less than 8 digits.)	**365**
2. Multiply that number by 3.	**365 x 3 = 1,095**
3. Add 15 to that result.	**1,095 + 15 = 1,110**
4. Multiply that answer by 2.	**1,110 x 2 = 2,220**
5. Divide that result by 6.	**2,220 ÷ 6 = 370**
6. Subtract his original number from that total.	**370 − 365 = 5**

Finally, tell him to hold the *back* of the calculator towards you. Pretend that you have the power to see through solid objects, and then announce the total that appears in the display. No matter which number your friend chooses, the final total will always be 5!

Variations

When repeating this trick, change Step 3 and the final total will be a different number.

Step 3

Add	3	6	9	12	15	18	21	24	27	30 →
Final total	1	2	3	4	5	6	7	8	9	10 →

TALKING CALCULATOR

Your friend secretly selects two numbers, works a few math problems, and hands you the calculator. When you hold the calculator up to your ear, it whispers the two numbers that she chose!

Materials

A calculator   Paper and pencil

Presentation

Have a friend write down a 1-digit number and a 2-digit number on a piece of paper without showing you.

Then hand her the calculator and ask her to:

	Example 6 & 82
1. Enter her 1-digit number.	**6**
2. Multiply that number by 5.	**6 x 5 = 30**
3. Add 5 to that answer.	**30 + 5 = 35**
4. Multiply that result by 10.	**35 x 10 = 350**
5. Add 20 to that total.	**350 + 20 = 370**

6. Multiply that result by 2.   **370 x 2 = 740**

7. Subtract 8 from that answer.   **740 – 8 = 732**

8. Add her 2-digit number to that result.   **732 + 82 = 814**

Finally, ask her to hand you the calculator with the final total. Say that you are going to activate the calculator's talking mode by entering a special code. Subtract 132, push =, and your friend's two numbers will appear in the display.

$$
\begin{array}{r}
8\ 1\ 4 \\
-\ 1\ 3\ 2 \\
\hline
\underline{6}\ \underline{8}\ \underline{2}
\end{array}
$$

Sneak a peek at the two numbers as you put the calculator up to your ear. Pretend that the calculator is whispering to you, and then announce your friend's two numbers!

An Exception
When you subtract 132 and get only two digits, your friend chose 0 for the 1-digit number.

$$
\begin{array}{ll}
\textbf{Example} & 159 \\
\textbf{0 \& 27} & \underline{-\ 132} \\
& 27 = \underline{0}\ \underline{27}
\end{array}
$$

SECRET CODE

Your friend thinks of an important date in his life, and then works a few problems on a calculator. When he is finished, you enter a magical secret code and his date suddenly appears in the display!

Materials

A calculator   Paper and pencil

Preparation

Write this month chart on a piece of paper.

1-Jan.	4-April	7-July	10-Oct.
2-Feb.	5-May	8-Aug.	11-Nov.
3-March	6-June	9-Sept.	12-Dec.

Presentation

Ask a friend to think of any important date in his life—his birthday, for instance, or a favorite holiday.

Hand him the calculator and tell him to:

	Example
1. Enter the number of the month from the month chart without letting you see it. (September = 9)	**Sept. 10** **9**
2. Multiply that number by 5.	**9 x 5 = 45**
3. Add 6 to that total.	**45 + 6 = 51**
4. Multiply that answer by 4.	**51 x 4 = 204**
5. Add 9 to that total.	**204 + 9 =213**
6. Multiply that answer by 5.	**213 x 5 = 1,065**
7. Add the number of the day. (Sept. <u>10</u>)	**1,065 + 10 = 1,075**
8. Add 700 to that total.	**1,075 + 700 = 1,775**

Finally, tell your friend to hand you the calculator with the final total. Just enter the secret code (minus 865 equals) and the important date that he thought of will magically appear! The first digit is the number of the month, and the last two digits are the number of the day.

$$\begin{array}{r} 1\ 7\ 7\ 5 \\ -\ 8\ 8\ 5 \\ \hline 9\ 1\ 0 \end{array}$$

↑ ↑

Sept. 10

An Exception
When you subtract 865 and get four digits, the first two digits are the number of the month.

Examples   1031 = <u>10</u> <u>31</u> = **Oct. 31**
1205 = <u>12</u> <u>05</u> = **Dec. 5**

FAMILY SECRETS

After a friend works a few problems on a calculator, you are able to divulge how many brothers, sisters, and grandparents she has!

Materials
A calculator

Example
4 brothers
3 sisters
2 grandparents

Presentation
Have a friend:

1. Enter her number of brothers in the calculator.

    4

2. Multiply that number by 2.

    4 x 2 = 8

3. Add 3 to that total.

    8 + 3 = 11

4. Multiply that answer by 5.

    11 x 5 = 55

5. Add her number of sisters to that total.

    55 + 3 = 58

6. Multiply that answer by 10.   **58 x 10 = 580**

7. Add her number of grandparents
to that total.   **580 + 2 = 582**

8. Add 125 to that answer.   **582 + 125 = 707**

Finally, tell her to hand you the calculator with the final total. Just subtract 275 and her number of brothers, sisters, and grandparents magically appear!

$$
\begin{array}{r}
7\ 0\ 7 \\
-\ 2\ 7\ 5 \\
\hline
\underline{4}\ \underline{3}\ \underline{2}
\end{array}
$$

brothers → **4 3 2** ← **grandparents**

↑

sisters

Exceptions

When you subtract 275 and get only two digits, your friend has no brothers.

Example: 12 = <u>0</u> 1 2 so number of brothers = 0.

When you subtract 275 and get only one digit, your friend has no brothers and no sisters.

**Example: 2 = <u>0</u> <u>0</u> 2 so number of brothers = 0
and number of sisters = 0.**

POCKET MONEY

After your friend works a few problems on a calculator, you are able to reveal his favorite number and how much loose change he has in his pocket!

Materials
A calculator

Presentation
Have a friend:

Example
Favorite Number-25
Loose Change-47¢

1. Enter his favorite number in the calculator. (This number must be five digits or less.)

25

2. Multiply that number by 2.

25 x 2 = 50

3. Add 5 to that answer.

50 + 5 = 55

4. Multiply that result by 50.

55 x 50 = 2750

5. Add the loose change in his pocket. (This amount must be less than $1.00)

2750 + 47 = 2797

6. Multiply that total by 4.

2797 x 4 = 11188

7. Subtract 1000 from that answer.

11188 − 1000 = 10188

Then, tell him to hand you the calculator with the final total. Just divide that total by 400 and your friend's favorite number and his loose change will magically appear!

$$10188 \div 400 = \underline{25.47}$$

Favorite number   **Loose change**

Exceptions

If you divide by 400 and there is only one number after the decimal point, add on a 0 to get the loose change.

Example: $311040 \div 400 = 777.6 = \underline{777.60}$
Loose change = 60¢

If you divide by 400 and there are no numbers after the decimal point, your friend has no loose change.

Example: $2800 \div 400 = 7. = \underline{7.00}$
Loose change = 0¢

SUBTRACTION SORCERY

You ask a friend to work a subtraction problem on a calculator. After she tells you just one digit of the answer, you are able to divulge the entire answer!

Materials
A calculator
Paper and pencil

Presentation   **Example**
Ask a friend to:

1. Write any 3-digit number on a piece of paper without letting you see it. Tell her that all three digits must be different.   **427**

2. Reverse this number and write it below the first number.   **724**

3. Subtract the two numbers on a calculator. Tell her to enter the larger number first.

$$\begin{array}{r} 724 \\ -\ 427 \\ \hline 297 \end{array}$$

Finally, ask her to tell you either the first digit or the last digit of the total. You are now able to divulge the entire answer!

How to Do it

Here are all the possible answers when you subtract two 3-digit numbers as described.

99   198   297   396   495   594   693   792   891
(099)

Notice that the middle digit is always 9 and that the sum of the first digit and the last digit is 9. So just subtract what your friend tells you from 9 to get the missing digit.

Example

She tells you the first digit is 2.

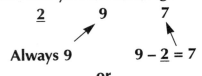

Always 9   **9 – 2 = 7**

or

She tells you the last digit is 7.

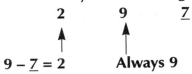

9 – 7 = 2   **Always 9**

An Exception

If your friend tells you that the first digit or last digit is 9, her answer will be 99.

CHAPTER FOUR
CALCULATOR
RIDDLES

The calculator that you own is a remarkable little machine. You've always known that it can perform mathematical calculations faster and with more accuracy than most humans, but did you know that it can also talk?

Yes, it's true! Your calculator will talk to you if you push the right buttons. For example, your calculator will tell you its name if you push clear and then *carefully* push **353 x 9 x 100 + 18 =** . Just turn your calculator *upside down*, and it will tell you!

Now that you and your calculator have been properly introduced, it's time to have some fun! Use the calculator alphabet below to help you find the answers to the math jokes and math riddles in this section. If you don't understand an answer, look at the explanation in the back of the book or just ask your calculator!

THE CALCULATOR ALPHABET

Upside-down numbers:	0	1	2	3	4	5	6	7	8	9
Letters:	O	I	Z	E	h	S	g	L	B	G

1. What is the only thing that gets larger the more you take away?

$$25{,}000 - 68 - 952 - 8{,}956 - 11{,}320 =$$

2. Which has fewer legs, a goose or no goose?

$$25.009 \div .001 + 10{,}000 =$$

3. Picture these U.S. coins: a nickel, a penny, and a dime. OK? Ellie's parents have 3 children. One is Nick and another is Penny. Who is the third?

$$.05 \div .01 \div .10 \times 3 \times 211 + 123 =$$

4. How many legs does a barbershop quartet have?

$$2 \times 2 \times 2 \times 10 \times 70 + 338 - .09 =$$

5. A pet store owner has 17 eels. All but 9 were sold. How many eels does the owner have left?

$$337.8 \times 17 - 9 =$$

6. Who weighs more, Lee the 5-foot (152 cm) butcher or Bob the 7-foot (213 cm) wrestler?

$$5 \times 7 \times 10 - 13 =$$

7. A doctor gave you three pills and said to take one every half hour. How long will the pills last?

$$3 \times .5 + 2.6 =$$

8. Which would you rather have, an old one-hundred-dollar bill or a brand-new one?

$$100 \times 77 + 118.001 - 100 =$$

9. Bob and Bill took a dividing test in school. Bob wore glasses and Bill did not. Who got a higher score on the test?

$$10 \times 10 \times 10 - 200 + 8 =$$

10. How many seconds are in a year?

$$31{,}557{,}600 \div 1{,}000{,}000 - 26.3476 =$$

11. A barrel of water weighed 100 kilograms, but after somebody put something in it, it weighed only 25 kilograms. What was put in the barrel?

$$500 \times 100 + 4{,}000 - 300 + 4 =$$

12. Bill subtracted numbers for 20 minutes, Bess multiplied them, and Leslie added them.

Who was more exhausted when they finished?

$$9 + 57 + 868 + 7{,}920 + 93{,}208 + 215{,}475 =$$

Who went into debt when they were finished?

$$17{,}865 - 9{,}438 - 607 - 95 - 7 =$$

Who got the most work done in 20 minutes?

$$.3 \times 2 \times 2.6 \times 20 \times 7.1 \times 25 =$$

13. What number did the math teacher bring the student who fainted?

$$222 \times .2 \div 2 - .2 - 20 =$$

14. What is the largest number that will fit in your calculator's display?

$$99{,}999{,}999 \div 9 - 11{,}058{,}162 + 656{,}060 =$$

15. Bob says that only one month has 28 days. His boss says that there are more. Who is right?

$$28 \times 29 \times 30 + 31 - 18{,}882.486 =$$

16. What did seven do that made all the other numbers afraid of it?

7 x .07 ÷ .7 x 7 + 1.9 =

17. What number never tells the truth when it is resting?

223,314 ÷ 7 ÷ 2 ÷ 3 =

18. How much dirt is in a hole that is 5-feet (152.5 cm) deep, 2-feet (61 cm) wide, and 3-feet (91.5 cm) long?

5 x 2 x 3 – 30 =

19. Take two eggs from three eggs and what do you have?

9,992 x .2 x 3 – 2 =

20. What part of a lame dog reminds you of what happens when you start adding 37 and 26?

$$224 \times 25 - 25.486 + 37 + 26 =$$

MATH PUZZLES
& GAMES

CHAPTER ONE
FANCY FIGURING

Get out your pencil. This chapter provides some old-fashioned arithmetic problems that call for serious ciphering. Now you can enjoy an assortment of brain-teasers that touch on such weighty mathematical concerns as *probability, recombinant shapes, number series,* and some just plain count-your-fingers figuring!

BULL'S-EYE

With your bow and arrow, shoot the following scores on the target using the smallest number of arrows: A. Shoot a 25. B. Shoot a 19. C. Shoot a 47.

JAWBREAKERS

Two jawbreaker-lovers stand at the vending machine with their pennies. The machine has 35 yellow jawbreakers and 35 blue jawbreakers. If they got a jawbreaker for each penny they put into the machine, how many pennies would they use before they had two jawbreakers of the same color?

Answers on page 238

ANTSY ANT

An ant decides to race along a ruler, starting at the 12-inch end. He runs from the 12-inch mark to the 6-inch mark in 12 seconds. How many seconds will it take him to reach the 1-inch mark?

A BURNED RECEIPT

This important receipt was badly burned in a fire. Can you reconstruct the missing digits so that the equation works?

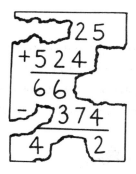

IN THE OLD CEMETERY

In the old cemetery, you stumble upon two tombstones. The dots indicate places where the stones are so worn that the dates have been erased. You find an old diary in the church and learn that both Mary and her brother John died in childhood and that the single missing digit in the bottom line of John's stone was one less than the single digit on Mary's. However, John lived *longer* than Mary. Calculate a possible birth year on Mary's stone.

Solution on page 238

MAGIC SQUARES

This ancient mathematical curiosity was once used as a charm to bring good fortune and protect against disease. Mathematicians now call it the *magic square*. It's magical because the square is constructed so that the numbers in each vertical column, horizontal row, and diagonal add up to the same number.

8	3	4
1	5	9
6	7	2

Third-Order Magic Square

16	3	2	13
5	10	11	8
9	6	7	12
4	15	14	1

Fourth-Order Magic Square

Magic squares can be of any order, beginning with a 3 x 3 square of nine numbers. In fact, any regular number sequence that you can place in a square (3 x 3, 4 x 4, 5 x 5, etc.) can be made into a magic square. The *magic constant* for a third-order square is 15. A fourth-order square has a constant of 34.

There are seven variations of a third-order (3 x 3) magic square, 880 variations of a fourth-order square, and over a million variations for a fifth-order square. Although it might seem difficult to construct anything larger than a third-order square, a French mathematician named Loubèrè came up with a trick for making any size of odd-order square. We'll use his method to build a simple fifth-order square.

A piece of large-grid graph paper comes in handy, since you'll be working on several squares at once, each one duplicating the original square.

Outline four neighboring 5 x 5 squares on your graph paper. You'll begin in the bottom left square. Write the number 1 in the top middle cell of that square. Write the number 2 diagonally above it to the right (in a new square), and repeat the number 2 at the bottom of that row (in the original square). Now write the number 3 diagonally to the right of the number 2, and repeat the number 3 above in the new square. Write the number 4 diagonally to the right of the number 3, and notice that another number 4 should appear in the first row of the original square, three cells from the top. When a cell is already occupied, place the next number in the cell directly below its preceding number, as in number 6.

Creating a Fifth-Order Magic Square

You should now begin to see a pattern emerge. Continue filling in the cells of your magic squares until you complete them. What is the magic constant for a fifth-order square?

17	24	1	8	15
23	5	7	14	16
4	6	13	20	22
10	12	19	21	3
11	18	25	2	9

Fifth-Order Magic Square

For a simple fifth-order square of this type, notice that the numbers proceed consecutively along the diagonal as the original square is duplicated.

You can perform all sorts of tricks with magic squares. Have a friend erase any number or series of numbers in the square and you can always replace them because you know the square's constant. Or have a friend completely rearrange all the numbers in a single row, column, or diagonal. Only you know the secret.

Solution on page 239

MORE MAGIC SHAPES

Similar to the magic square puzzles, these shapes rely on overlapping number relationships for their unusual qualities.

For the magic triangle, arrange the numbers 4 through 9 in the circles so that every side of the triangle equals 21.

For the magic daisy, place the numbers 1 through 11 in the circles so that every straight line of three circles totals 18.

For the magic star, place the numbers 1 through 12 in the circles so that each straight row of four circles adds up to 26. In this case, you may find more than one solution.

Magic Triangle

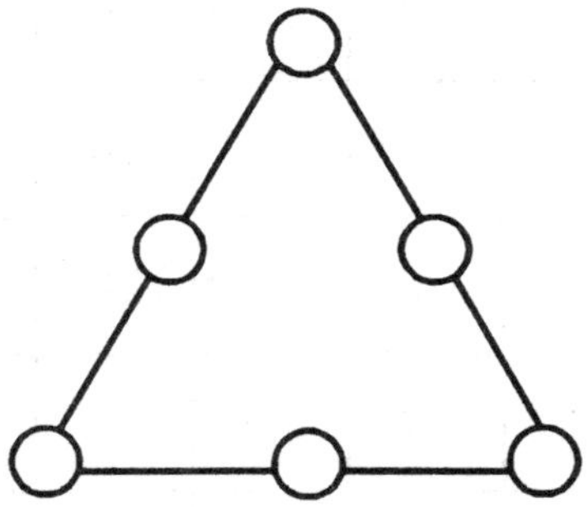

Magic Daisy

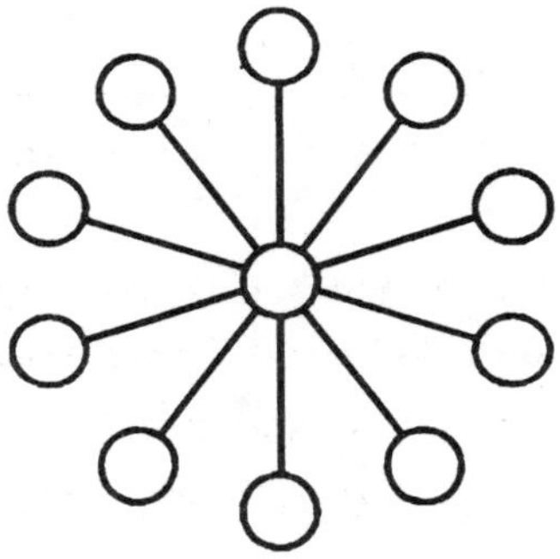

Magic Star

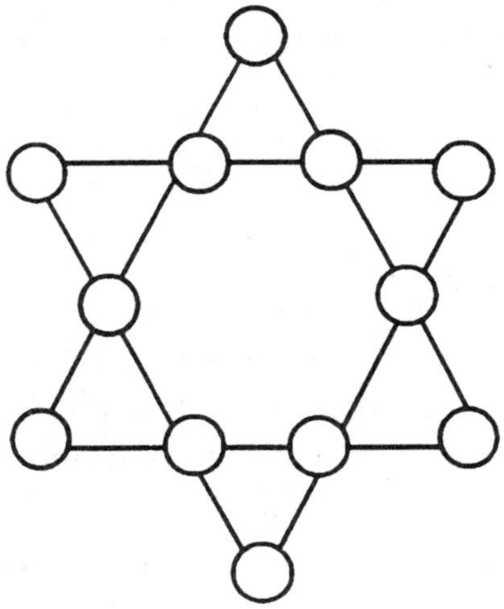

Solution on page 239

Ben Franklin's Wheel

Benjamin Franklin, the great American inventor, scientist, philosopher, and statesman, was also a maker of magic squares. He preferred to design them as wheels, however, and the one reproduced below represents one of his more elaborate designs. It was supposedly doodled one tedious afternoon when the young Franklin was a clerk at the Pennsylvania Assembly.

Knowing what you now know about magic squares, fill in all the missing numbers.

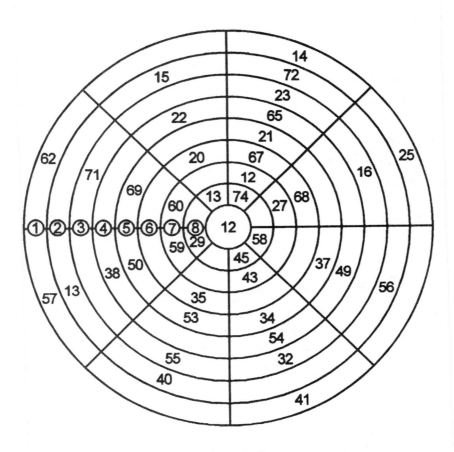

Magic Wheel

Solution on page 239

The Chimes of Big Ben

Big Ben, London's largest clock, calls out the time with loud chimes, one for each hour. If it takes Big Ben 3 seconds to chime three times at three o'clock, how long will it take Big Ben to chime six times at 6 o'clock?

Solution on page 239

Count the Streetlights

On opposite sides of a street, there are 45 streetlights, each one at a distance of 30 yards from the other. The streetlights on one side are arranged so that each lamp fills a gap between two other streetlights on the opposite side. How long is the street?

Weighing In

How many pounds does each cube, pyramid, and sphere weigh when each row has the combined weight indicated?

$$\square \; \square \; \triangle \; \bigcirc = 17$$

$$\square \; \triangle \; \triangle \; \bigcirc = 14$$

$$\square \; \triangle \; \bigcirc \; \bigcirc = 13$$

Solution on page 240

CHAPTER TWO
MATH LOGIC PUZZLES

Beginning Puzzles

Fishing

Four men went fishing. They caught six fish altogether. One man caught three, another caught two, one caught one, and one didn't catch anything. Which man caught how many fish? What did each of the fishermen use for bait?

1. The one who caught two fish wasn't Sammy nor the one who used worms.
2. The one who used the flatfish didn't catch as many as Fred.
3. Dry flies were the best lure of the day, catching three fish.
4. Torkel used eggs.
5. Sammy didn't use the flat fish.

	Number of Fish Caught				**Lures**			
	zero	one	two	three	worms	eggs	flatfish	dry flies
Fred								
Sammy								
Torkel								
Joe								
worms								
eggs								
flatfish								
dry flies								

See answers on page 241

Jump Rope

Some kids were jumping rope (double Dutch) at the school break. They counted how many times each one jumped before missing. See if you can figure out how many jumps each kid made. (You may want to use a pencil and paper to do the adding and subtracting needed to solve this brainer.)

1. Gary jumped eight fewer times than Arnie.
2. Combined, Danielle, and Ruth jumped 37 times.
3. Jan jumped 8 more jumps than Danielle.
4. Gary and Danielle are separated by just three jumps.
5. Arnie's jumps number 5 more than Danielle.

	9	12	17	20	25
Danielle					
Gary					
Jan					
Arnie					
Ruth					

See answers on page 242

Pocket Change

Five boys went to the store to buy some treats. One boy had $4. One boy had $3. Two boys had $2, and one boy had $1. Using the following clues, determine how much money each boy started with and how much each had when he left the store.

The clues are:

1. Alex started with more than Jim.
2. Scott spent 15¢ more than Dan.
3. Duane started with more money than just one other person.
4. Alex spent the most, but he did not end with the least.
5. Dan started with 66% as much as Scott.
6. Jim spent the least and ended with more than Alex or Dan.
7. Duane spent 35¢.

	Started With				**Ended With**				
	$4	$3	$2	$1	1.65	95¢	70¢	40¢	10¢
Alex									
Scott									
Dan									
Jim									
Duane									

See answers on page 243

Temperature

A sixth-grade class project involved keeping track of the average temperature of the classroom over a two-week period in January. The results of the study showed that, at one particular time of the day, the temperature was always at its lowest point. Try to figure out when, during the day, the temperature was lowest, and the reason for it.

1. The automatic heating system in the school comes on at 6:00 in the morning.
2. No students arrive before 8:30. The first temperature reading takes place at that time.
3. The temperature is taken at half hour intervals from 8:30 until 3:00 in the afternoon, when the students go home.
4. The automatic heating system goes off at 2:00.
5. The highest temperature reading is at 10:00.
6. The 2:30 reading of the temperature shows a cooling off, but not the lowest temperature.
7. Morning recess is from 10:20 to 10:35.
8. Afternoon recess takes place from 1:45 until 2:00.
9. The highest temperature over the two-week period was 74 degrees F (23.3 degrees C).

So, when *was* the temperature at its lowest, and why?

See answer on page 243

Easy Puzzles

Coast to Coast

Jacques and Chi Chi rode bikes across the United States. They stopped at several major cities along the way. Figure out where they went and the order in which they visited the cities based on the coordinates given in the clues below. (The visited city is the one "closest" to the intersection of the coordinates.)

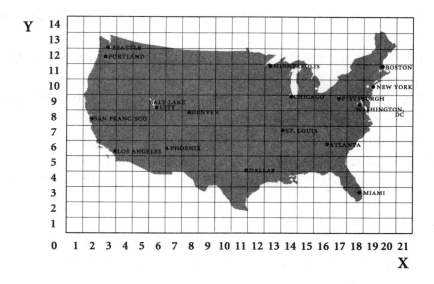

They started their journey at X6, Y5.5

Their first stop was at X3, Y5.5; then they rode on to X1.5, Y7.5.

Then they stopped off in the city at X2.5, Y11.5.

From there they rode to X5.5, Y8, and then to X7.5, Y8.

They stayed a few days at X11, Y4, and three days at X13, Y6.5.

From there they rode to X13.5, Y9, then to X16.5, Y9.

Finally, tired but happy, they ended their journey at X18, Y8.5.

Start to finish, what are the eleven American cities visited by Jacques and Chi Chi?

See answers on page 240

Coffee

A few friends meet each morning for coffee. For one of them, it is the only cup of coffee all day. For another, it's only the first of eight cups. Zowie!

Your challenge is to figure out how many cups of coffee each person drinks per day, how many sugar lumps they use per cup, and whether or not they put in milk.

1. Jan uses three times as many lumps as the person who drinks four cups.
2. Three people, including the one who uses four lumps, use no milk.
3. The one who drinks 1 cup a day (not Max) drinks his coffee black without sugar.
4. Doris uses both milk and sugar.
5. Max, who uses no milk, uses half as many sugars as the person who drinks twice as many cups as he does.
6. Boris drinks two more cups than Jan, but Jan uses two more sugars than Boris.

	Cups					Lumps of Sugar					Milk	
	1	4	5	6	8	0	1	2	4	6	Yes	No
Max												
Doris												
Blizzo												
Jan												
Boris												

See answers on page 240

Decimal Ruler

This ruler measures inches but, instead of measuring them in the usual way, in sixteenths, it measures them in *tenths*. In other words, the standard inch is divided into ten (decimal) units, rather than sixteen units.

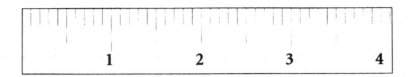

When we measure something with this decimal ruler, it is expressed as the number of inches plus the tenths. For example, the line just below measures 3.4 inches. Go ahead, check it out (mark the length on a straight piece of paper and then hold it next to the ruler).

Now, using paper and this ruler, measure these other lines:

a _____

b _____

c _____

d _____

e _____

f _____

g _____

Check your measurements in the solutions.

See answers on page 241

Destry's Missing Numbers

Destry has five boxes, shown below. Each is supposed to have a decimal number in it, but they're all empty! Help Destry find his missing numbers and put them back in their boxes.

Here are some clues to where the numbers should go:

1. One square (the sum of 11.09, 6.21, and 5.04) is to the left of a square with the difference between 13.27 and 1.34.
2. C is not 13.47 but another square is.
3. One square has a number larger than square B by 13.78.
4. The square with a sum of 13.62, 3.98, 7.00, and .57 is between B and E.
5. The smallest number is B; the largest is E.

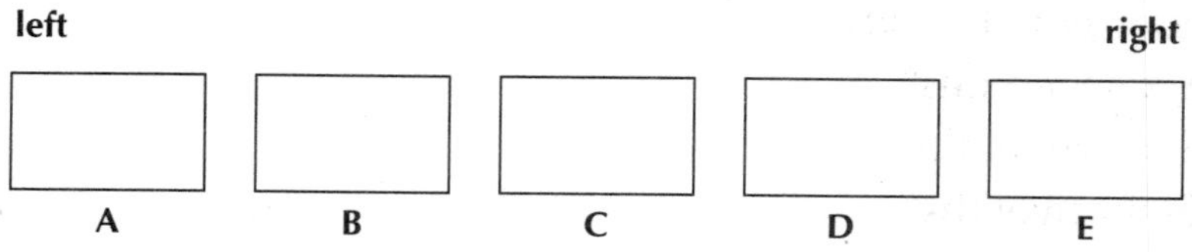

left   **right**

A	B	C	D	E

See answers on page 241

E.F. Bingo

Four girls—Lorraine, Michelle, Wanda, and Sheila—are in a serious game of E.F. Bingo (E.F. stands for equivalent fractions). The first one to fill in a line on her card (up-and-down, across, or diagonally) wins. To solve this puzzle, figure out which girl wins and gets to yell "Bingo!"

The fractions come up and are called in this order:

1. "Four twentieths"
2. "Eighteen twenty-seconds"
3. "Four tenths"
4. "Six tenths"
5. "Two eighths"
6. "Ten sixteenths"
7. "Twelve fourteenths"
8. "Four twenty-eighths"
9. "Six sixteenths"
10. "Six twentieths"
11. "Eight twelfths"
12. "Sixteen eighteenths"
13. "Four twelfths"

E.F. Bingo cards

$1/4$	$3/8$	$1/8$
$6/7$	$1/3$	$2/10$
$4/5$	$3/5$	$4/10$

Lorraine

$2/5$	$2/3$	$1/6$
$1/7$	$4/5$	$3/8$
$1/2$	$3/9$	$2/6$

Michelle

$5/8$	$2/10$	$2/6$
$6/7$	$8/9$	$3/7$
$1/3$	$1/4$	$9/11$

Wanda

$1/2$	$5/8$	$3/10$
$1/4$	$1/3$	$2/12$
$2/6$	$4/10$	$2/3$

Sheila

See answer on page 241

Famous Person

There's a famous person's name spelled out in the twelve boxes below. Using the coding provided, figure out the letters of the name and solve this puzzle.

A=1	G=7	N=14	U=21
B=2	H=8	O=15	V=22
C=3	I=9	P=16	W=23
D=4	J=10	Q=17	X=24
E=5	K=11	R=18	Y=25
F=6	L=12	S=19	Z=26
	M=13	T=20	

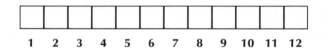

1 2 3 4 5 6 7 8 9 10 11 12

Clues:

Boxes 7 and 10 are U − P

Box 2 is C x E

Boxes 4, 8, and 9 are the same letter: F + J − B

Box 6 is Z − Y + J

Box 12 is E^2

Box 1 is O − E

Box 5 is X ÷ D

Box 11 is G x C − Q

Box 3 is T + E + D

See answer on page 241

Flighty Decimals

Normally trustworthy and reliable, the decimals below got a little out of hand. They escaped from their geometric shapes and were scattered all over the place! Now the decimals are all lined up in two rows (below) in order from largest to smallest, but they really need to be put back into their proper geometric places. Your job is to do just that.

5.20	4.39	4.01	3.71	2.60	1.42
1.16	1.01	.72	.30	.07	.03

Here are clues to where the decimals are to go (four decimals in each shape) in the geometric spaces below:

1. 4.39 and 4.01 are supposed to be in the same figure; 5.20 (the ringleader) is supposed to be in a different one.
2. Decimals 3.71 and 1.01 are together in the rectangle.
3. The total in the circle, where .07 is supposed to be, is 6.46.
4. The smallest total comes from the rectangle, where .30 is supposed to be.
5. The difference between the totals of the square and the circle is 5.96.
6. Decimal 1.16 is supposed to be in the circle.

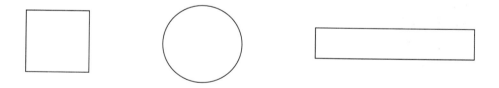

Add the decimals assigned to each shape and check your totals against the solution.

See answers on page 241

Heather's Garden

Heather's Garden is out of control! She planted it just so, and then went to surfing at a beach. When she got back from her trip, she found the turnips mixing with the cabbages, the pole beans mixing with the carrots, and the rows jumbled all over the place. Plus, field mice have gotten in and some of the garden is missing!

Heather had made a map so she would remember how much she planted where, but the mice got that too! See if you can reconstruct the garden's contents for her.

1. The most rows are neither spinach nor cabbages.
2. There are two more rows of carrots than turnips and two more rows of spinach than carrots.
3. There are four more rows of spinach than turnips.
4. There aren't as many rows of pole beans as "cukes" (cucumbers in garden talk).
5. There is one less cabbage row than spinach.
6. Heather doesn't like turnips so much, so she planted just one row (mostly to sacrifice to the mice, but they don't care all that much for turnips, either!).

Rows

	1	2	3	4	5	6
pole beans						
cabbages						
carrots						
cucumbers						
spinach						
turnips						

See answers on page 241

Mathathon

Several girls were trying to work some math problems. Several boys said they could help them find the solutions. The girls said, "Fat chance!". So there was a contest between the girls and the boys to see who was best at solving the problems. Check it out and see who won.

Each problem is worth 10 points if the answer is correct; −5 points if it is wrong.

Problem **1**   9 x .3 =
  The girls said 2.7, the boys said 2.7.
Problem **2**   1.06 + .089 + 11.2 + 6.34 =
  The girls said 18.689, the boys said 18.768.
Problem **3**   ½ + ¾ =
  The girls said 1¼, the boys said 1.25.
Problem **4**   13.88 − 6.96 =
  The girls said 6.92, the boys said 7.92.
Problem **5**   4.003 x 99 =
  The girls said 396.297, the boys said 386.297.
Problem **6** $2\frac{1}{3}$ x ½ =
  The girls said 1.166, the boys said .765.
Problem **7**   .33 ÷ 3 =
  The girls said .11, the boys said 1.1.
Problem **8**   6.66 + 3.75 + 9.07 =
  The girls said 19.48, the boys said 19.38.

So, who was best at doing math — or at least at working these particular problems?

See answer on page 242

Mountain Climb

Dacon and his friends all went mountain climbing this summer, but not together. They climbed different mountains. Using the clues, see if you can figure out who climbed which mountain, and the heights of the mountains they climbed.

1. Dacon climbed higher than 4500 feet, but not on Goat.
2. Jake climbed higher than both Macom and the one who climbed Sleepy.
3. The mountain which is 9000 feet is not Old Baldy or Goat.
4. The shortest mountain was not climbed by Bacon.
5. Mirre is shorter than the mountain climbed by Macom, but higher than the one climbed by Drakon.
6. Sleepy is not the tallest, but taller than Goat.
7. Raleigh is taller than Goat, which is taller than the ones climbed by Drakon and Dacon.

	Elevation					Mountain				
	9000	8000	7500	11000	4500	Old Baldy	Mirre	Raleigh	Sleepy	Goat
Dacon										
Drakon										
Macom										
Bacon										
Jake										
Old Baldy										
Mirre										
Raleigh										
Sleepy										
Goat										

See answers on page 242

Mountain Race

Five people will race to the tops of mountains of different heights. To have a fair race, each person will carry a weight; the person climbing the lowest mountain, the heaviest backpack weight, etc.

Using the clues, figure out each person's full name, the mountain each will climb, and the weight to be carried in each backpack.

1. Paul's pack weighs 30 lbs.
2. Andy's mountain is 865 ft. higher than the one Brown is climbing.
3. Gerald's pack weighs the same as Dale's minus McGee's.
4. Stiller's pack is half as heavy as the person's climbing Mt. Morgan.
5. Jim's and Dorsey's packs combined weigh 60 lbs.
6. Anderson's pack is 20 pounds lighter than Dale's.

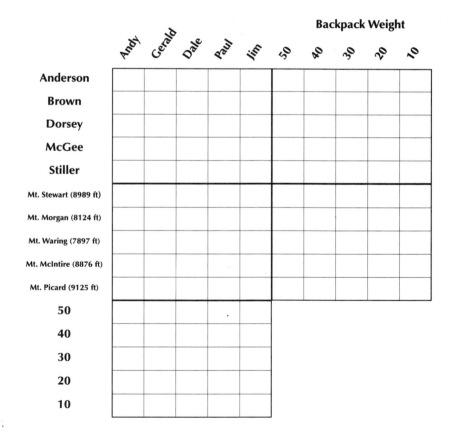

See answers on page 242

Ned's Newspaper Route

Ned delivers papers in his neighborhood. In January he had 43 customers. He wanted to make a little more money, so he went door to door, and by April he had found five new customers. One new customer gets just a daily paper, two get just a Sunday paper, and two get both. What you need to do is figure out which of his new customers gets what, and the color of their houses (which helps Ned to keep track of things).

1. The Simpsons get both papers; their house is not white.
2. The Browns' house is neither gray nor the color of one of the houses that gets just the Sunday paper.
3. The customer's name who subscribes to just the daily paper begins with J.
4. The customer in the green house does not get a Sunday paper.
5. Mr. Johnson lives in the blue house.

	Papers			House Color				
	Sunday	daily	both	grey	green	white	yellow	blue
Jones								
Johnson								
Smith								
Brown								
Simpson								
grey			
green			
white			
yellow			
blue			

See answers on page 242

CHAPTER THREE
PENCIL PUZZLERS

BROKEN PENTAGRAM

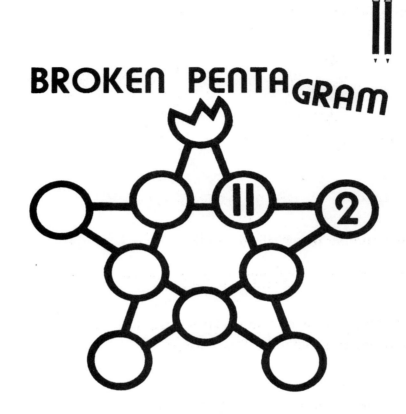

It's possible to position ten consecutive numbers on an unbroken pentagram of ten circles in such a way that each straight line of four circles totals exactly the same number. Here we issue the same challenge but with a little twist. Of ten consecutive numbers place nine in the nine unbroken circles in such a way that each straight line of three or four unbroken circles totals exactly twenty-four. Two numbers have been positioned for you.

Solution on page 244

(Need a clue? Turn to page 130.)

SQUARE SHOOTER

A standard checkerboard measures 8 squares by 8 squares and contains 32 black squares and 32 red squares. Exactly 139 other size checkerboards, ranging from 2 by 2 to 7 by 7 squares, exist on a standard checkerboard. How many of these smaller-size checkerboards can be found, that also contain an equal number of red and black squares.

Solution on page 244

THE $10,000 PYRAMID

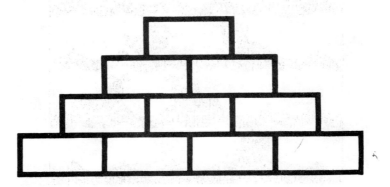

Using only the number four, place ten money amounts in the ten blocks of this pyramid to total $10,000.

Solution on page 244

Clue to the puzzle on page 128: Throw out the number five.

SITTING DUCKS

There are three different kinds of ducks in this puzzle. Position six more ducks on this two-dimensional pond so that each of the five horizontal and vertical rows will sport all three different kinds of sitting ducks.

Solution on page 244

CASE CLOSED

Before you are nine cases labeled with the letters "E", "F", "S" or "T". It is known that inside each case is a different number that begins with the letter seen on the outside of the case. Example: "T" could stand for two, three, ten, and so on. It is your challenge to determine all nine numbers to reveal a magic square in which each horizontal, vertical, and diagonal row of three cases totals exactly the same.

Solution on page 244

(Need a clue? Turn to page 135.)

OPTICAL DIVERSION

Using the numbers one through nine three times each, number the remaining surfaces of the cubes in such a way that each cube totals exactly fifteen. In doing so, you must also assure that each row of four cube surfaces in a straight row and facing the same direction (up, left, or right) must total twenty. Example: The two cube surfaces three and four above are in a straight line, facing left. There are nine such rows to be completed.

Solution on page 244

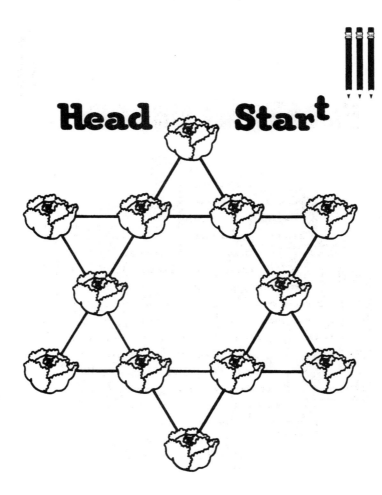

Head Start

These twelve heads of lettuce are planted in such a way as to create six straight rows each containing four heads of lettuce. Can you plant a garden using another configuration which fulfills these same requirements?

Solution on page 244

(Need a clue? Turn to page 136.)

FLOATING HEDGES #2

Draw a continuous line through this maze which connects the numbers one through eight consecutively. You may never travel the same passageway more than once.

Solution on page 244

Clues to the puzzle on page 132: Each row totals 36, the smallest number used is four.

Round Numbers #1

Position one letter in each of the five between-spoke openings on this wagon wheel. Do this in such a manner that three numbers are spelled out that total thirteen. Words may be written clockwise and counter-clockwise and, as in traditional crossword puzzles, individual letters may be shared. Example: On a larger wheel, four and five could be written: R-U-O-F-I-V-E.

Solution on page 244

Clue to the puzzle on page 134: Begin with a square four-by-four grid. Then eliminate four lettuce heads.

MAGIC WORD SQUARES

Each letter in this puzzle represents a different number from zero to nine. It is your challenge to switch these letters back to numbers in such a way that each horizontal, vertical, and diagonal row of three words totals the same number. Your total for this puzzle is 1515. It is known that "tab" is the highest scoring word and "raw" is the second highest scoring word.

Solution on page 245

(Need a clue? Turn to page 139.)

ARROWHEADINGS

In this maze, your course headings are predetermined and point values have been assigned to each passage. Starting from the bottom intersection, travel to each of the other five intersections and return to the beginning intersection with the lowest possible point score.

Solution on page 245

(Need a clue? Turn to page 141.)

Wicked Number

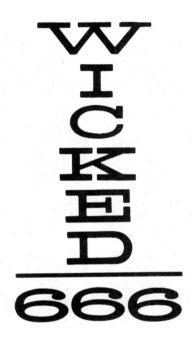

At present this puzzle really only totals 601. That's because three of the letters in "wicked" do not belong. You must eliminate the bogus letters and substitute the correct three letters to achieve the desired total.

Solution on page 245

Clue to the puzzle on page 137: DAD = 505.

EQUATOR XING

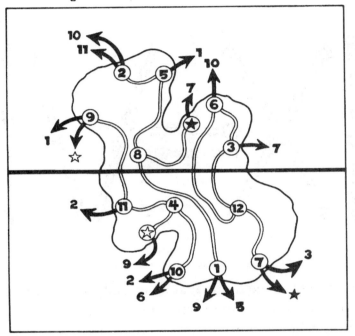

There are twelve numerical destinations (1 through 12) on this tiny tropical island. You must start your journey at one of the two stars and then travel to each number on the map and ultimately finish at the other star. At no time may any number be visited more than once. Throughout your journey you may only cross the equator a total of nine times: four by land, five by sea. Sea routes are illustrated by arrows which indicate your optional destinations.

Solution on page 245

MATCH WITS #2

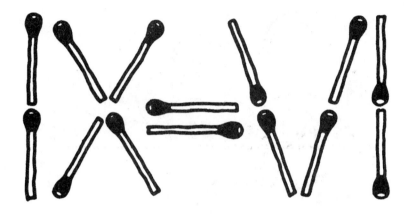

At present we see an equation that incorrectly tells us that the Roman numeral nine is equal to the Roman numeral six. Can you add three additional matches to this equation to make both sides equal?

Solution on page 245

Clue to the puzzle on page 138 : Lowest score possible is forty-five points.

3 RING CIRCUIT

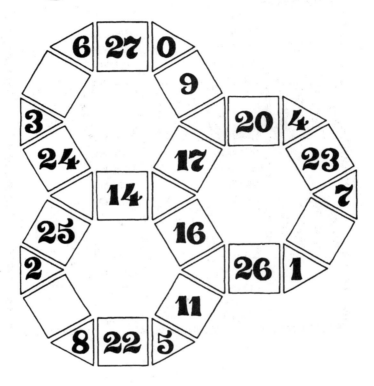

When this puzzle is completely solved, it will reveal the numbers zero through twenty-seven. All you have to do is position the remaining seven numbers to assure that each of the three rings of twelve numbers totals exactly the same number.

Solution on page 245

Key Decision #2

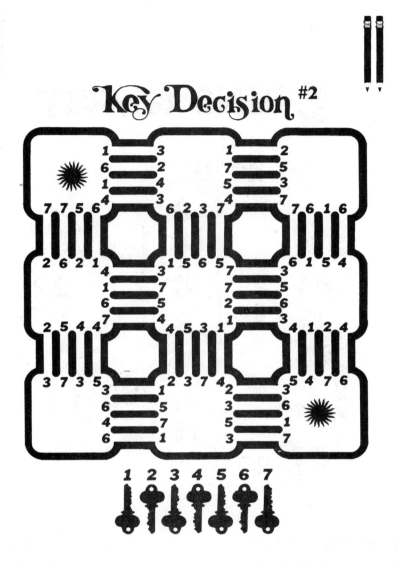

The numbered keys above correspond to the locked corridors in the puzzle. It is your challenge to select only three keys that will unlock the correct corridors and allow passage from one sunburst room to the other.

Solution on page 245

Trace Track

The numbers in this puzzle show the current position of four cars on this crisscrossing race track. As the three outer turnabout panels are currently arranged, only car 1 can cross the finish line. Rearrange three of the four turnabout panels around the center section of track to construct a single unending track that utilizes all road surfaces and will allow all cars to finish in the order 1,2,3,4. Cars may not pass one another on this final lap.

Solution on page 246

NUMERIC SHELVES

Rearrange the sixteen numbers in this puzzle to allow the two horizontal and two vertical rows of five squares to total the same number. There are twelve solvable totals. Your tasks are to construct the highest possible and lowest possible totals.

Solution on page 246

Lucky Lady

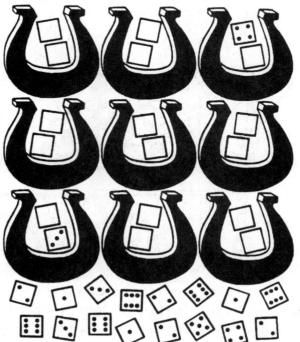

Nine pairs of dice are positioned in nine horseshoes in this puzzle. The pips are missing from all but two dice. From the illustrated sixteen dice you must add the pips to the blank dice to satisfy the following conditions: 1) Each horseshoe must total a different number. 2) Each horizontal, vertical, and diagonal row of three horseshoes must total twenty-one. 3) Doubles may not appear in any horseshoe.

Solution on page 246

Chapter 4
Grid & Dot Games

Squiggling Snake • The Cop & the Robber
Springing Sprouts • Hare & Hounds • The Ratcatcher
Horse Race • Daisy Petals • Black & White

All games are mathematical in that they present both a problem and a method for solving the problem. Board games like checkers or chess depend on the competing player's powers of calculation. Games that use playing cards, number wheels, or dice combine the player's skill with the laws of probabilty. Most games teach us about what mathematicians call *quantum operations*. This means that players must repeat small, uniform steps to reach a solution within a given framework of laws. So, playing a game of checkers isn't very different from solving a math puzzle.

SQUIGGLING SNAKE

In this game, players take turns joining dots by a line to make one long snake. No diagonal lines are allowed. Each player adds to the snake at either end, and a player can only add to his opponent's segment, not his own. The first player to make the snake close on itself loses the game.

Here's how an actual game might be played. To tell the two player's apart, one player draws straight lines, and the other player draws squiggly lines.

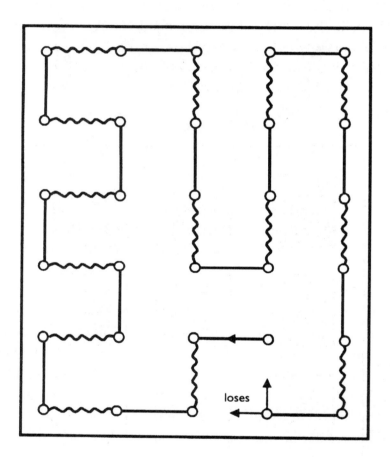

THE COP & THE ROBBER

On a piece of cardboard or construction paper, draw the game board below including the letters C (cop) and R (robber). This board represents a city grid of several blocks and streets, and the letters indicate the starting position of the cop and robber.

You need two different coins, one for the cop and one for the robber. Start with each coin on its letter. The cop always moves first. After that, robber and cop take turns moving. A player moves a coin one block only, left or right, up or down — that is, from one corner to the next. The cop captures the robber by landing on the robber in one move. To make the game a little more challenging, the cop must capture the robber in twenty moves or less, or the robber wins.

Hint: There is a way for the cop to nab the robber. The secret lies in the bottom right corner of the grid.

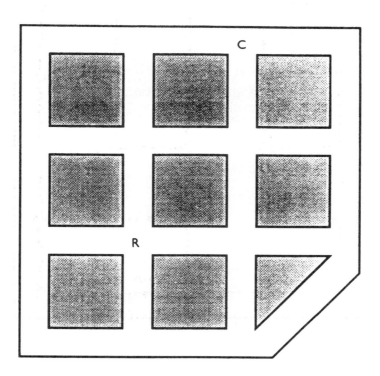

SPRINGING SPROUTS

Most mathematical games are played on grids, but some of the newer ones use *topology*, the geometry of flexible lines and surfaces, as a starting point. Springing Sprouts was invented in the 1960's by a mathematician at Cambridge University in England. Not only will you enjoy playing it, but your finished game makes an interesting piece of artwork!

The first player begins by drawing three spots (A). The second player must connect two of the spots with a line (remember, the line can be curved) and then adds a new spot somewhere along that line (B).

No lines may cross (C), but a player may connect a spot to itself in a loop — as long as he adds another spot (D).

A spot "dies" when three lines lead to it and no more lines can connect to it. To indicate a dead spot, darken it (E).

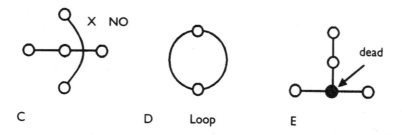

A player wins by drawing the last connecting line so that all the remaining spots are dead and the second player can no longer connect them. Here's a sample game, won by player A in seven moves.

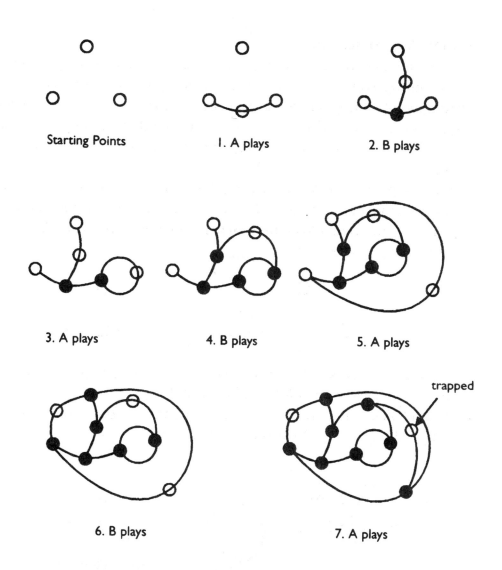

Starting Points

1. A plays

2. B plays

3. A plays

4. B plays

5. A plays

6. B plays

7. A plays

trapped

Mathematicians have tried to figure out how many moves it takes for either player to win Springing Sprouts. They've discovered, but not yet proved, that the number lies between twice and three times the number of spots you start with. Starting with three spots, for instance, the game can continue for six to nine moves. Starting with four spots, the game may last for eight to twelve moves, and so on.

HARE & HOUNDS

Many board games involve "hunting." This one was a favorite of Victorian schoolchildren. Games like this teach us about geometrical figures called trapezoids, which are four-sided figures with only two sides parallel. The corners of *trapezoids*, or *vertices*, also play an important part in this game.

Use a ruler to draw the board on a piece of paper or cardboard. At every place where the lines meet in a corner, draw a small circle. Draw a large A at the left side of the board and a large B at the right side.

Player #1 has one coin, representing the Hare, and Player #2 has three coins, representing the Hounds. The game starts with Player #1

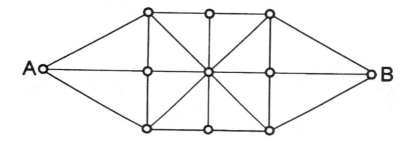

placing his Hare on circle A. Player #2 follows by placing one of his Hounds on any other circle. He will use the next two turns to place his other Hounds on circles, as the Hare moves from circle to circle, trying to escape.

The Hounds may move in any direction forward (that is, towards circle A) or up and down, but not towards circle B. The aim of the Hare is to reach the safety of circle B while the Hounds, of course, try to block his way and prevent him from moving.

THE RATCATCHER

This is another version of a strategic chase-and-capture game. One player has twelve Rats, and the other player is the Ratcatcher. The game starts with the thirteen pieces in the positions shown below, the white dot representing the Ratcatcher.

Both Ratcatcher and Rats can move in any direction onto an empty intersection of lines (*vertex*). The Ratcatcher can remove a Rat from

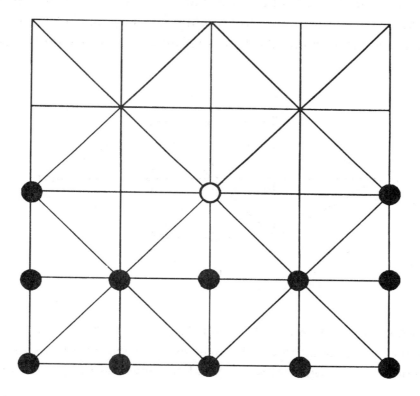

the board by jumping over him to an empty vertex on the other side. But the Rats can gang up on the Ratcatcher by surrounding him in such a way that he can neither move nor jump.

HORSE RACE

In this ancient Korean racing game, *nyout*, players throw one of a pair of dice (a die) to determine the number of moves, then race their buttons, or "horses," around the circular track illustrated below. Notice that the track has five large squares, sixteen smaller squares, and eight circles.

The players start at square A, and the first player to return to square A wins the game. When a player throws the die, he may only move up to five spaces; a throw of six must be thrown again. If a player's horse lands on one of the larger squares B, C, or D, the horse may take a shortcut through the circle to reach A.

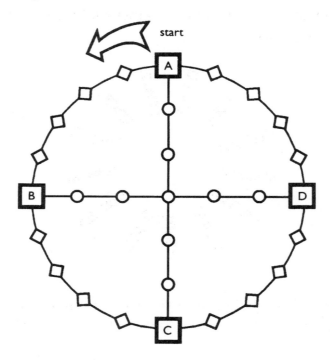

Each player may have up to three horses, but both players must have the same number of horses to ensure a fair game. A player may choose to add another horse instead of moving his original horse.

If one player's horse lands on a square already occupied by another of his own horses, both horses may move together in all the following moves. If one player's horse lands on a square occupied by his opponent's horse, the opponent's horse is removed and must reenter the race.

To win the game, a player must throw the exact number to get each of his horses back to A. It usually takes three or four times around the track before one player's horses win. And your fortunes may reverse at any time!

DAISY PETALS

On piece of paper or cardboard, construct a thirteen-petal daisy using crayons for the petals.

Two players take turns plucking either one petal apiece, or two neighboring petals apiece. The player who plucks the last petal wins the game.

Remember, a player can only take two petals if the petals are neighbors. The player who makes the second move can always win this game if he has a sharp eye and knows something about the principle of *symmetry*— that is, the balance of parts on opposite sides of a line or about a center point.

BLACK & WHITE

One player alone can enjoy this game, or two players can compete to see who can finish in the least number of moves.

Reproduce the board below with two 3-inch-square pieces of paper, joined at the corner and lined in a grid pattern. In squares on the left side of the board, place eight black pieces (buttons or pennies will do). In the squares on the right side of the board, place eight white pieces.

The object of the game is to exchange the positions of the black and white pieces in the least possible number of moves. You can move a piece by sliding it to a neighboring empty square, or by jumping over a neighboring piece of either color. This can be done in exactly 46 moves, but you can still consider yourself an expert if you finish in 52 moves or less.

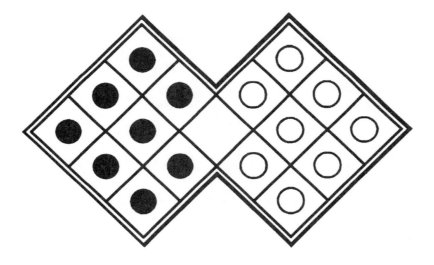

CHAPTER FIVE
MATH LOGIC PUZZLES

MEDIUM PUZZLES

Auction

The Clydesdale County Fair held its annual fund-raising auction last week. Five of the people who bought items are listed here.

Your challenge is to match the last names of the purchasers with their first names, identify which items each one bought, and figure out how much each one paid (the lowest amount that anyone paid was $3.50).

Here are a few clues:

1. Elroy is not Grey.
2. The man who bought the coffee paid the highest price, twice that of the fruit.
3. The cheese sold for $2.00 less than the coffee and was purchased by Black.
4. Ms. Green bought the pie for $2/3$ the cost of the cake.
5. White and Duane shared their cake and coffee.
6. The pie cost $0.50 more than the fruit.
7. Dan paid $6.00 for his item.
8. Neither Elroy, Denise, nor Black paid over $5.00.

Solution on page 240

Last Name **Purchase**

	Green	White	Black	Brown	Grey	cake	pie	fruit	cheese	coffee
Irene										
Denise										
Duane										
Dan										
Elroy										
$										
$										
$										
$										
$										
cake										
pie										
fruit										
cheese										
coffee										

Hint: Start by working out the prices as early as possible.

Biology Class

Kristi and five of her friends have each adopted an animal in the biology class at their high school. Using the clues listed below, see if you can figure out which animal (the W's) belongs to which student (the K's).

1. Walter can fly; Willy can't.
2. Kristi's animal is 14 cm (6 in) long.
3. The ladybug is not a lady, nor the smallest.
4. Willy is 5 cm (2 in) shorter than the largest animal.
5. Kyle's animal is neither a fly nor a ladybug.
6. Walter is 10 cm (4 in) shorter than the bat, who's 3 cm (about 1 in) shorter than Wendy.
7. Wanda is the largest.
8. Kurt's animal is the smallest.
9. The hamster belongs to Kevin.
10. Willy is neither the rat nor the hamster.
11. Weldon, who is able to fly, belongs to Kristen.
12. Kate's adoption measures 18 cm (7 in).

Solution on page 240

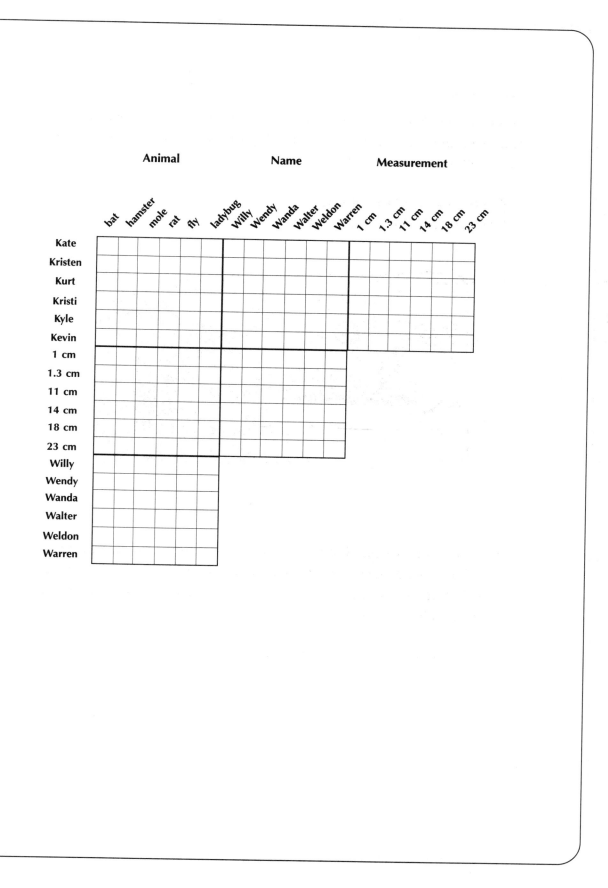

Chicken Mountain

At the top of Chicken Mountain live five chicken farmers. Each farmer thinks his chickens are the best. Farmer McSanders sas his chickens are best because they lay the most eggs. Farmer Saffola says his chickens make the best fryers.

See if you can figure out which farmer does have the best chickens, based on the following facts plus the formula provided to grade the chickens.

1. The chickens with the best feathers live on the McCombe farm. They sell for $0.73.
2. The chickens which sell for $0.64 produce 105 eggs per day. It's not the Poularde farm.
3. Farmer Saffola has 500 chickens.
4. The farm which produces 115 eggs per day sells its chickens for $0.71.
5. The smartest chickens live on the McPlume farm.
6. The best fryers get the most money.
7. Farmers McSanders and McPlume have 833 chickens between them.
8. The smallest farm produces the most eggs and the second-best price.
9. The biggest chickens produce 4.8 eggs per chicken on the Poularde farm.

Solution on page 240

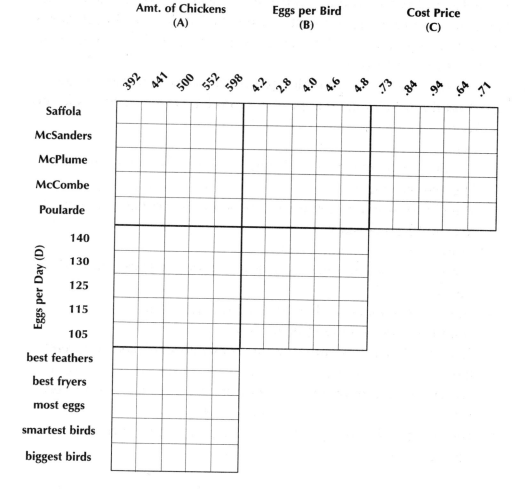

| | Amt. of Chickens (A) | | | | | Eggs per Bird (B) | | | | | Cost Price (C) | | | | |
	392	441	500	552	598	4.2	2.8	4.0	4.6	4.8	.73	.84	.94	.64	.71
Saffola															
McSanders															
McPlume															
McCombe															
Poularde															
140															
130															
125															
115															
105															
best feathers															
best fryers															
most eggs															
smartest birds															
biggest birds															

Eggs per Day (D)

**Best Chickens on
Chicken Mountain
Grading Formula:**

A ÷ B x C + D

Chocolate Chip Cookies

Five of the world's foremost chocolate chip cookie bakers arrived for the annual Cookie Fiesta. While the bakers all agreed on most of the ingredients that go into their famous chocolate chip cookies, they did not agree at all on the right number of chips per cookie or the amount of time they should be baked to come out perfect. Determine the full names of the five cookie bakers, the number of chips each puts in her cookies, and how long they leave them to bake.

Here are a few clues:

1. Ms. Strudel bakes her cookies for 17 minutes, 7 seconds.
2. Effie uses 2 chips fewer than Ruby does.
3. Ms. Applestreet bakes her cookies 51 seconds longer than Thelma does.
4. Ms. Spicer uses one less chip than Ms. Applestreet puts in her cookies.
5. Ms. Honeydew uses more chips than Ms. Spicer does.
6. Ruby isn't Ms. Honeydew.
7. Ms. Spicer bakes for less time than do either Miriam or Georgia.
8. The woman who bakes her cookies for 17 minutes, 7 seconds uses 7 chips.
9. Georgia bakes hers for 17 minutes and 8 seconds, 1 second longer than Ruby does.
10. The person using 5 chips isn't Ms. Spicer.

Solution on page 240

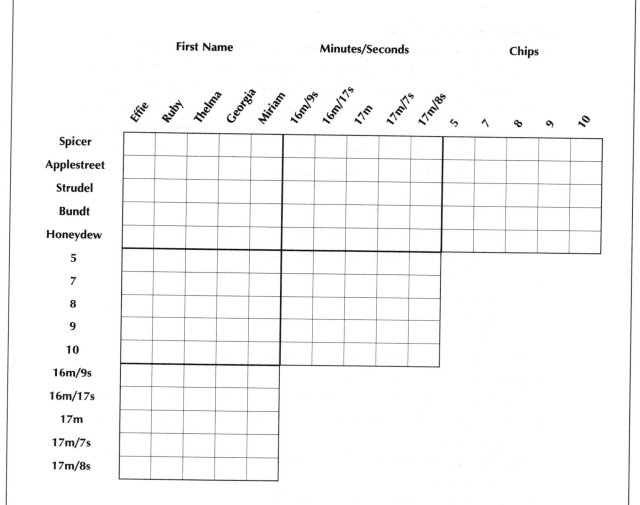

First Name: Effie, Ruby, Thelma, Georgia, Miriam

Minutes/Seconds: 16m/9s, 16m/17s, 17m, 17m/7s, 17m/8s

Chips: 5, 7, 8, 9, 10

Spicer
Applestreet
Strudel
Bundt
Honeydew
5
7
8
9
10
16m/9s
16m/17s
17m
17m/7s
17m/8s

Hint: Clues 4, 5 and 10 are the key ones.

Dog Apartments

Six dogs live in the Airedale Apartments. Each dog lives on a different floor, eats a different amount of dog food (in pounds) each week, and takes a different number of baths each month. Using the clues below, figure out which floor each dog lives on, the amount of food each one eats, and the number of baths each one takes. Watch out for tricks!

1. The dog in 221 eats twice as much as the one who takes 1 bath a week.
2. MacTavish eats four pounds less than Spunky, but takes five more baths.
3. The dog that eats 32 pounds a month takes 3 baths a week.
4. Wilfred lives two floors above Spunky. Spunky lives two floors above Chico.
5. Taz and the dog on the 6th floor eat a combined weight of 80 pounds in a month.
6. The dog in 341 eats 24 pounds a month and bathes once a week.
7. The dog in 408 eats fewer pounds in a month than he takes baths.
8. The dog on the 5th floor eats 16 pounds a month and takes one less bath than Chico.

Solution on page 241

	Apartment No.						Food per Week						Baths per Month					
	103	221	341	408	512	609	2	4	6	8	10	12	2	3	4	6	9	12
MacTavish																		
Chico																		
Ivan																		
Wilfred																		
Taz																		
Spunky																		
Baths 2																		
3																		
4																		
6																		
9																		
12																		
Food 2																		
4																		
6																		
8																		
10																		
12																		

Lunch at Paul's

Paul invited some friends for lunch and asked each to bring two items. Everyone already had one item and they brought that, but they had to buy a second item at the store. Using the clues and the price list below, figure out who brought which items, and how much each person spent—including Paul, who bought the coffee.

Purchased Items	Price List
chicken	$6.40 pound
coffee	$5.50 pound
cheese	$4.80 pound
mayonnaise	$1.09 per 8-oz jar
bread	$1.39 loaf

1. Julie bought 9 ounces of one of her items, which cost her $2.70. She did not bring fruit.
2. The person who brought the salad also bought three loaves of bread.
3. Sandra bought two 8-ounce jars of mayonnaise but did not bring the fruit or the cake.
4. Paul needed pickles and salad. Wally brought one of them.
5. Diane's purchase was 12 ounces and it cost her $4.80.
6. The person who paid $2.75 for half a pound also brought the olives.

Solution on page 242

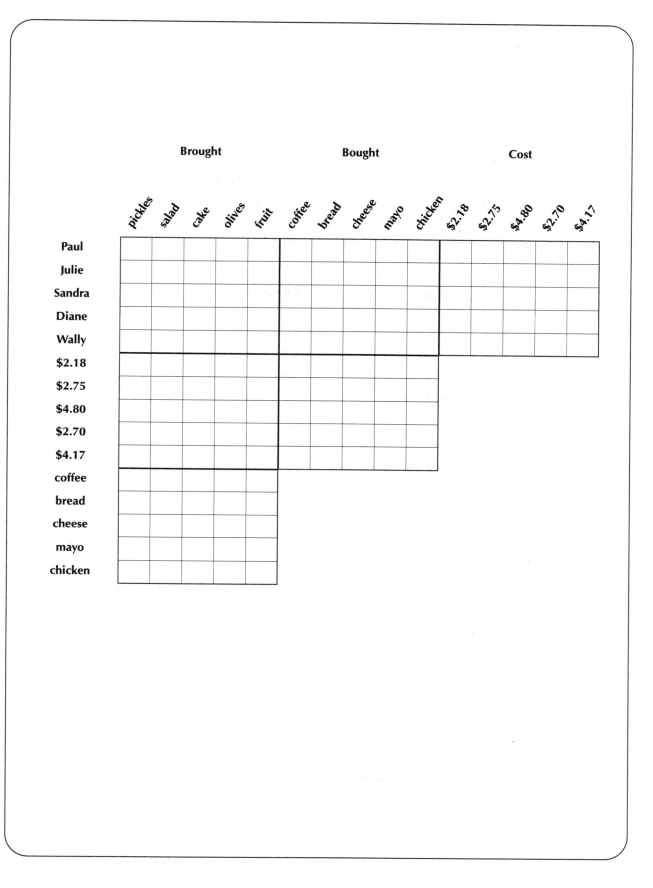

Multiplication Jeopardy

For a change, Dale and some friends studying for a multiplication test gave each other the problem answers (products) and tried to figure out the two numbers in the problem. From the clues, figure out each student's full name, the product each was given, and the correct multiplier and multiplicand. One of the products (where multiplicand and multiplier intersect) is 144.

1. Dale's multiplicand is 14.
2. Tina's last name is not Johns.
3. June's multiplier is 9.
4. Neil is neither James nor Jones.
5. Miss Jensen's product is 120.
6. The person whose multiplicand is 13 is not James, Jensen, or Mr. Johnson.
7. Tina's product is 143.
8. Neil's multiplicand is 18. His product is 126.
9. Johns's multiplier is 7.

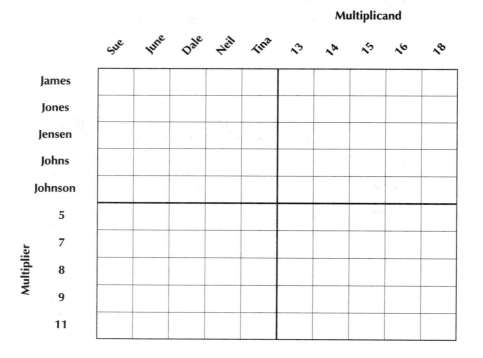

Solution on page 242

Old House

Six different families have lived a total of 88 years in an old house. The original owners lived there half the total number of years. A second family lived there a quarter of the years. The third family lived in the house half that. Then a family lived there five years. The fifth family lived there two years. And the sixth family still lives there.

Each family painted the house a different color. Right now, it is white. How long did each family live in the old house? What color did each family paint it?

1. The Smiths lived there eleven times longer than the Parkers.
2. The house was yellow for two years.
3. In all, the house was painted three different colors—blue, yellow, and white—for 11 years.
4. The color was changed from green to brown after the Carpenters moved.
5. The house was either brown or red for 33 years.
6. The Barneses lived there longer than the number of years the house was blue and white.
7. The house was yellow when the Warners moved in.

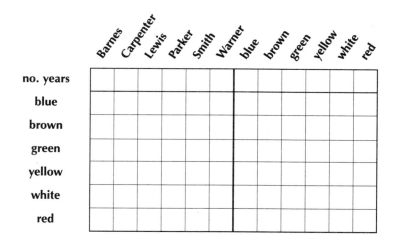

Solution on page 243

Play Ball

Toddy and some of her friends in a writing class had to bring a ball, representing their favorite sport, to class along with a composition that they had written about the sport. Toddy brought the ball weighing the least.

From the clues below, figure out who brought which ball, how much each ball weighed (in ounces), and what color it was.

1. The golf ball weighed less than the ball that Tanya brought, and also less than the brown ball.
2. Tom's ball weighed more than the red one.
3. The soccer ball, which was 14.5 ounces heavier than Teresa's ball, was not orange.
4. The person who brought the orange ball was not Teddie, whose ball weighed 15.2 ounces more than the Ping-Pong ball.
5. The ball that weighed more than all of them except for one was white.
6. The heaviest ball was the basketball, and the lightest one was yellow.
7. The 2-ounce ball was green, and smaller than the red one and the ball brought by Teddie.
8. The ball brought by Tillie was ten times heavier than the golf ball.

Solution on page 243

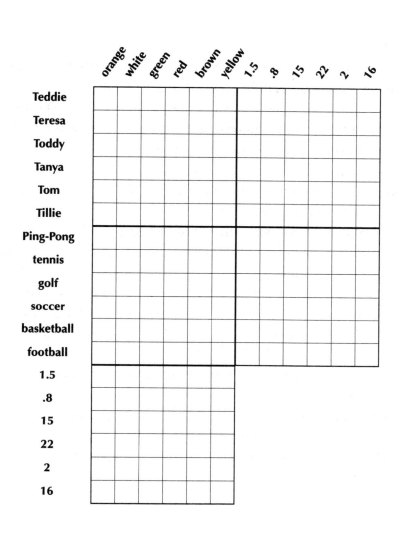

Potato Chips

Everyone in Mr. Glitzwhizzle's classroom agreed that no one could eat just one potato chip, but decided to have a contest to see who could eat the most in three minutes. Five students, and Mr. Glitzwhizzle himself, entered the race. From the clues below, figure out the last names of the students and Mr. Glitzwhizzle's first name, and how many bags of chips (the small size) each one ate.

1. Witteyspooner and Gazelda together didn't eat as many bags as Elmo or Jones did.
2. Hubert ate twice as many bags as Grugenminer.
3. Sally's last name does not start with G.
4. Kettledrummel ate one-fourth as many bags as Hubert did.
5. Mr. Glitzwhizzle ate 18 bags. Gerald could eat only half that many.
6. Hubert ate as many bags as Elmo and Gazelda combined.

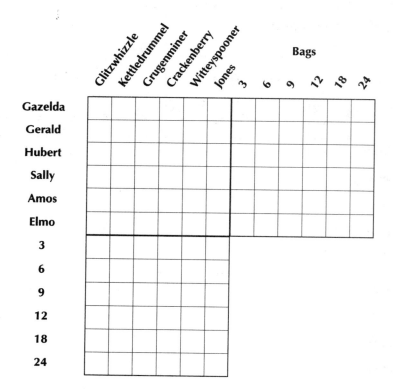

Solution on page 243

Queen Rachel's Bridge Toll

When the new Queen Rachel Bridge was built across the Queen Rachel River, Queen Rachel decided to charge a toll. Each person who crosses the bridge is charged .05 of the value of their shoes! So, if a person's shoes are worth $1.00, that person has to pay 5¢ in toll. With the information below, figure out how much each person has to pay to cross the Queen's bridge, and the color of their shoes.

1. Kurt's shoes are not green, nor is green the color of the shoes worth $3.60.
2. The person with the blue shoes must pay 36¢ toll.
3. Taber pays a higher toll then Cindy. Neither of them wears black shoes.
4. The person whose shoes are worth $3.60 is not Caleb.
5. One person, whose shoes are not green or red, pays an 18¢ toll.
6. The person with the red shoes pays 14¢ toll.
7. Caleb pays 24¢.
8. The person with the white shoes pays 38¢ toll.
9. Cindy's shoes are blue.

	Value of Shoes					Shoe Color				
	$2.80	$3.60	$4.80	$7.20	$7.60	red	green	blue	white	black
Chiquita										
Cindy										
Kurt										
Taber										
Caleb										
red										
green										
blue										
white										
black										

Solution on page 243

Skateboard Contest

Five kids in the finals of the Fossil Street skateboard contest ride their boards from home to the site for the event. From the clues provided, figure out the kids' full names, the number of blocks each has to ride to the contest, and the street on which they live.

1. Chestnut Avenue is 4 blocks farther away than where Roger lives.
2. Ms. Mander lives on Main Street, 8 blocks away from Lenny.
3. Cooper lives 3 blocks from Linden and 7 blocks from Kenny.
4. Chapman lives six blocks farther away than 11th Street.
5. Kenny, whose last name starts with "L", lives closer than Sally.
6. Jimmy lives on Elm Street.

Blocks from Fossil St.

	Jimmy	Sally	Lenny	Roger	Kenny	1	3	7	8	11
Linden										
Lyle										
Mander										
Cooper										
Chapman										
Elm St.										
Main St.										
Chestnut Ave.										
Acorn Dr.										
11th St.										
1										
3										
7										
8										
11										

Solution on page 243

CHAPTER 6
MIND-BENDING
MATH PUZZLES

Sox Unseen

Sam's favorite colors are blue and green, so it's not surprising that he has six blue sox and six green sox in his sock drawer. Unfortunately, they are hopelessly mixed up and one day, in complete darkness, he has to grab some sox to wear.

How many sox does he have to take from the drawer to make sure he gets a matching pair—either green or blue? (For some strange reason, his mother insists that his socks have to match!)

Solution on page 246

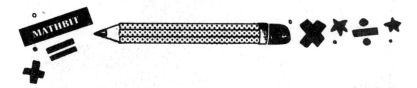

Add numbers to make squares:

1 =	1 = 1 x 1
1 + **2** + 1 =	4 = 2 x 2
1 + 2 + **3** + 2 + 1 =	9 = 3 x 3
1 + 2 + 3 + **4** + 3 + 2 + 1 =	16 = 4 x 4
1 + 2 + 3 + 4 + **5** + 4 + 3 + 2 + 1 =	25 = 5 x 5
1 + 2 + 3 + 4 + 5 + **6** + 5 + 4 + 3 + 2 + 1 =	36 = 6 x 6
1 + 2 + 3 + 4 + 5 + 6 + **7** + 6 + 5 + 4 + 3 + 2 + 1 =	49 = 7 x 7

Gloves Galore!

Gloria's favorite colors are pink and yellow. She has sox in those colors, of course, but she *really* likes gloves!

In her glove drawer, there are six pairs of pink gloves and six pairs of yellow gloves, but like Sam's sox, the gloves are all mixed up. In complete darkness, how many gloves does Gloria have to take from the drawer in order to be sure she gets one pair? She doesn't mind whether it's a pink or yellow pair.

(Hint: This may sound a bit like Sox Unseen, *but watch out! Gloves are more complicated than sox.)*

Solution on page 246

Birthday Hugs

"O frabjous day! Calloo Callay!"*
　　　　　　It's Jenny's birthday!

Jenny invites her three best friends Janey, Jeannie, and Joany to come to a party at her house, and when they all arrive they all give each other hugs.

　How many hugs is that altogether?

*A special "gold star" if you can name the work and author of this famous line.

Solution on page 246

The last joint of your thumb is probably close to an inch long, measuring from nail to knuckle. The spread from the tip of your thumb to the tip of your forefinger is probably five or six inches. Measure them with a ruler–then you can use these "units" to measure the lengths of all sorts of things.

Sticky Shakes

For John's birthday celebration, he invites six friends—Jack, Jake, Jim, Joe, Julian, and Justin—to a favorite burger place where they order thick and sticky milk shakes: banana, chocolate, maple, peanut butter, pineapple, strawberry, and vanilla.

While they slurp the shakes, their hands get sticky. Laughing about "shake" hands, they decide to actually do it—shake hands with their shake-sticky hands. So each boy shakes hands once with everyone else. How many handshakes is that altogether?

Solution on page 246

The Wolf, the Goat, and the Cabbage

You are traveling through difficult country, taking with you a wolf, a goat, and a cabbage. All during the trip the wolf wants to eat the goat, and the goat wants to eat the cabbage, and you have to be careful to prevent either calamity.

You come to a river and find a boat which can take you across, but it's so small that you can take only one passenger at a time—either the wolf, or the goat, or the cabbage.

You must never leave the wolf alone with the goat, nor the goat alone with the cabbage.

So how can you get them all across the river?

Solution on page 246

Floating Family

Mom and Dad and two kids have to cross a river, and they find a boat, but it is so small it can carry only one adult or two kids. Luckily both the kids are good rowers, but how can the whole family get across the river?

Solution on page 247

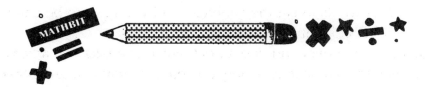

Did you know that most drinking glasses and cups have a circumference greater than their height? Test it out on some you have at home.

Take a piece of string and wrap it carefully once around a glass. You will almost always find the string is longer than the height of the glass. When is this not true?

Now you can amaze your friends by predicting this fun mathematical fact with one of their glasses before you measure it!

Slippery Slopes

Brenda the Brave sets off to climb a mountain which is 12,000 feet high. She plans to climb 3000 feet each day, before taking overnight rests. A mischievous mountain spirit, however, decides to test Brenda's resolve. Each night, Brenda's sleeping bag, with her soundly asleep in it, is magically moved 2000 feet *back down* the mountain, so that when Brenda awakes in the morning she finds herself only 1000 feet higher than she was the morning before!

Not one to give up, Brenda eventually succeeds. But how many days does it take her to reach the summit?

Solution on page 247

The Long and the Short of the Grass

Mr. Greengrass wants his lawn to be tidy and likes the grass cut short. Because he doesn't like mowing but wants to be able sit outside and read the paper on Sunday mornings and be proud of the smooth lawn, he decides to hire some good young mowers.

Two kids agree to mow Mr. Greengrass's grass on Saturdays for 15 weeks. To make sure they come every single Saturday, he agrees to pay them, at the end of the 15 weeks, $2 for every week that they mow it—as long as they will give him $3 for every week they miss.

At the end of the 15 weeks, they owe him exactly as much as he owes them, which is good news for Mr. Greengrass, but a rotten deal for the kids! How many weeks did they miss?

Solution on page 247

When drawing a graph, some people can never remember which is the x-axis and which is the y-axis. Here's a neat way to remember: say to yourself, "x is *a cross*."

Sugar Cubes

The Big Sugar Corporation wants to persuade people to use lumps of sugar, or sugar cubes; so they run a puzzle competition. The first person to get the answers right (the puzzle is made up of three parts) wins free sugar for life! Here's the puzzle:

You have been sent a *million cubes* of sugar. Yes, that's right, 1,000,000 sugar cubes! Each cube is just half an inch long, half an inch wide, and half an inch high.

1.Suppose the cubes arrived all wrapped up and packed together into one giant cube. Where could you put it? Under a table? In the garage? Or would you need a warehouse? *(Hint: What you need to work out is: How many little cubes would there be in each direction? And how long, wide and high would the giant cube be?)*

2.Now, suppose you decide to lay the cubes all out in a square on the ground—all packed together but this time only one layer deep? How big a space would you need? Your living room floor? A tennis court? Or would you need a parking lot the size of a city block?

3.Now for the big one. Pile all the million cubes one on top of the other into a tower just one cube thick. (You'll need *very* steady hands and not a breath of wind!) How high will the pile be? As high as a house (say 25 feet)? As high as New York's Empire State Building (1472 feet)? As high as Mount Adams (12,000 feet) in Washington State or Mount Everest (29,000 feet)? Or will the pile of cubes reach the moon (240,000 miles)?

Solutions on page 247

Crackers!

Mad Marty, crazy as crackers, invites his friends to a cracker puzzle party. The puzzle he sets them is this: How many different kinds of spread can you put on a cracker?

Everyone brings a different kind of spread and Marty supplies a gigantic box of crackers. Then they all get down to business:

Marty has a cracker with mayo =   1 spread

Pete brings peanut butter; so now
they have: (**1**) mayo, (**2**) peanut
butter, (**3**) mayo and peanut
butter =   3 spreads

Jake brings jelly; so now they have
   (**1**) mayo, (**2**) peanut butter,
   (**3**) mayo and peanut butter,
   (**4**) jelly, (**5**) jelly and mayo,
   (**6**) jelly and peanut butter,
   (**7**) jelly and mayo and
   peanut butter =   7 spreads

Hank brings honey =   how many
                                                    spreads?

Charlie brings cheese =   how many
                                                    spreads?

Fred brings fish-paste =   how many
                                                    spreads?

Solution on page 247

Crate Expectations

You have six bottles of pop for a party, and you want to arrange them in an attractive pattern in the crate. Four will make a square . . .

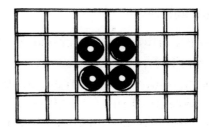

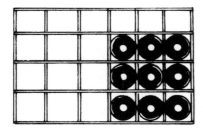

and nine will make a square. But six is a trickier number. How about an even number of bottles in each line?

Can you arrange them so that, in every row and in every column, the number of bottles is even (0, 2, 4, or 6)?

(Hint: This is quite tricky, and a fine puzzle to challenge your friends with. A good way to practice is to draw a grid on a piece of paper and use coins instead of bottles.)

Solution on page 247

Take It Away!

This is a game for two players. You will need someone to play against. It's a simple game, but the winning plan is really cunning. See if you can work it out just by playing the game.

You need about 12 or 15 small things—marbles, cookies, hard candies, pencils. It doesn't matter what they are, as long as they are all roughly the same size. Put them in a pile between the two players.

The first player takes either 1 or 2 things; then the second player takes 1 or 2 things, and they continue playing in this way. The winner is the player who takes the *last* thing.

For example, in a game starting with 14 pencils:

Player A takes 2	leaving 12
Player B takes 2	leaving 10
Player A takes 2	leaving 8
Player B takes 1	leaving 7
Player A takes 1	leaving 6
Player B takes 2	leaving 4
Player A takes 1	leaving 3
Player B takes 1	leaving 2
Player A takes 2 and wins	

OK, try it with a friend.

Solution on page 247

Oddwins

Here is another game for two players. You need 11 small objects—cookies, pebbles, paper clips.

Put the pile of objects between the players, and play alternately. First Player A takes either 1 or 2 objects. Then Player B takes 1 or 2 objects. Continue until all the objects have been taken.

The winner is the player who, at the end of the game, has an ODD number of objects—either 5 or 7.

Solution on page 247

Most people have a "wingspan" almost exactly equal to their height. So if you are 4 feet 10 inches high, then you will probably find that you measure 4 feet 10 inches from fingertip to fingertip with your arms stretched right out as far as they will go. Get a friend to help you measure your wingspan and check. Then you can use your wingspan as a measuring tool.

Witches' Brew

Three witches were mixing up a dreadful mathematical spell in their cauldron, and one of them—Fat Freddy—was reading out the recipe to the others.

Eye of newt and toe of frog
Wool of bat and tongue of dog

Suddenly they realized they needed some liquid—2 pints of armpit sweat. They had a bucketful of sweat, a saucepan that when full held exactly 3 pints, and a jug that when full held exactly 1 pint. How could they get exactly 2 pints?

(Hint: Try filling the pan, and then filling the jug from it.)

Solution on page 247

Witches' Stew

Many years later the same witches, now even older and more haggard, were mixing up a super-disgusting stew in their cauldron:

Adder's fork and blind worm's sting
Lizard's leg and howlet's wing...

And once again they needed to add the sweat, mixed this time with tears. They had a bucketful of liquid, and they needed to add exactly 4 pints, but all they had to measure it was a pitcher that held exactly 5 pints and a pot that held exactly 3.

How could they measure out exactly 4 pints?

Solution on page 247

Cookie Jars

Joe and Ken each held a cookie jar and had a look inside them to see how many cookies were left.

Joe said, "If you gave me one of yours, we'd both have the same number of cookies."

Ken said to Joe, "Yes, but you've eaten all yours, and you haven't any left!"

How many cookies does Ken have?

Solution on page 247

Fleabags

Two shaggy old dogs were walking down the street.

Captain sits down and scratches his ear, then turns to Champ and growls, "If one of yours fleas jumped onto me, we'd have the same number."

Champ barks back, "But if one of yours jumped onto me, I'd have five times as many as you!"

How many fleas are there on Champ?

Solution on page 248

Frisky Frogs

Across a stream runs a row of seven stepping stones.

On one side of the stream, sitting on the first three stones, are three girl frogs, Fergie, Francine, and Freda, and they want to get across to the other side.

There's an empty stone in the middle.

On the other side are three boy frogs, waiting to come across the other way—Fred, Frank, and Frambo.

Only one frog moves at a time. Any frog may hop to the next stone if it is empty, or may hop over one frog of the opposite sex on to an empty stone.

Can you get all the frogs across the river?

Solution on page 248

Leaping Lizards

Across a stream runs a row of eight stepping stones.

On one side of the stream, on the first five stones, sit five girl lizards—Liza, Lizzie, Lottie, Lola, and Liz—and they want to get across to the other side.

There's one empty stone in the middle.

On the other side are three boy lizards, waiting to come across the other way—Lonnie, Leo, and Len.

Only one lizard moves at a time. Any lizard may hop to the next stone if it is empty, or may hop over one lizard of the opposite sex onto an empty stone.

Can you get all the lizards across the river, and what's the smallest number of leaps?

Solution on page 248

Many spiders weave beautiful roundish webs, with a single strand spiraling out from the center. These amazing creatures keep the distances and turns so exact. Watch for webs on damp and frosty mornings and count the radial lines used in its construction.

Old MacDonald

Old MacDonald had a farm, EE-I-EE-I-OH!
And on that farm he had some pigs, EE-I-EE-I-OH!
With an *Oink oink!* here, and an *Oink oink!* there.
Here an *Oink!* There an *Oink!*
Everywhere an *Oink oink!*
Old MacDonald had a farm, EE-I-EE-I-OH!

Old MacDonald had some turkeys, too (certainly with a *Gobble gobble* here and a *Gobble gobble* there).

One day, while out feeding them all, he noticed that, if he added everything together, his pigs and his turkeys had a total of 24 legs and 12 wings between them.

How many pigs did Old MacDonald have? And how many turkeys?

Solution on page 248

Old Mrs. MacDonald

Mrs. MacDonald was a farmer too. She kept the cows and chickens. One day when she went out to feed them she counted everything up, and found that her animals had a total of 12 heads and 34 legs.

How many cows did she have? How many chickens?

Solution on page 249

Wiener Triangles

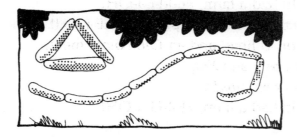

In the link-wiener factory in Sausageville , the wieners are made in long strings, with a link of skin holding each sausage to the next one. So, although the wieners are firm, you can bend the string of wieners around into many shapes. For example, you can easily bend a string of three wieners into a triangle.

Suppose you had a string of 9 wieners. Without breaking the string, how many triangles can you make?

Solution on page 248

If you use a combination lock, you can easily work out how long it will take a thief to try all the numbers and open it. If it has four dials with 10 digits on each, then there are a total of 10,000 different combinations. If the thief takes one second to try each, it will take nearly three hours to go through every number, since in three hours there are 3 x 60 x 60 seconds, or 10,800 seconds. On average, though, a thief will reach your secret number in half that time—say an hour and a half.

Tennis Tournament

You successfully arranged a "knock-out" tennis tournament, in which the winners of the first round meet in the second round, and so on. The little tournament had only four players, so arranging it was easy.

In the first round, Eenie played Meanie, and Eenie won. Miney played Mo, and Mo went through to the second round. In the second round—the final—Mo beat Eenie, and won the tournament.

The 3-game match card looked like this:

1st round	2nd round	winner
Eenie		
	Eenie	
Meanie		
		Mo
Miney		
	Mo	
Mo		

The match was so well organized, you've been asked to arrange another knock-out tennis tournament. This time 27 players enter. How many matches will have to be played to find the winner?

Solution on page 249

The Power of Seven

Far back in history, a lonely fort was being desperately defended against thousands of attackers.

The attacks came regularly at noon every day, and the defending commander knew he had to survive only three more days, for then would come the end of the attackers' calendar, and they would all go home to celebrate, giving time for his reinforcements to arrive.

He also knew that the attackers held an unshakable belief in the power of the number seven. So he always placed seven defenders on each wall of the fort. With three attacks to come, and only 24 defenders, he places 5 along each wall, and 1 in each corner tower.

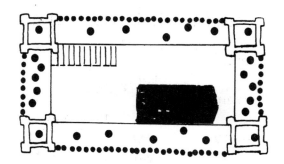

The attackers charge in from the north, and see seven defenders along that wall. Firing a volley of arrows, they wheel round in retreat, chanting "Neves! Neves!" meaning seven in their language. They charge from the west and again see seven defenders facing them. Firing a volley of arrows they retreat again. "Neves! Neves!"

From the south and then the east, again they charge. Each time they are met by exactly seven defenders. Each time they turn and flee, chanting "Neves! Neves!" And the attack is over for the day.

The commander mops his worried brow as the bugler blows the bugle to signal "Well done and all clear!" Then he learns the arrows have killed four of his men.

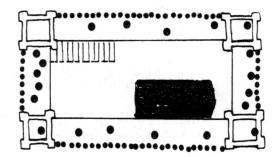

How can he rearrange the remaining 20 so that by noon of the next day there will still be 7 defenders on each side?

The Power of Seven continues

At noon on the second day the pattern of attack is different; the attackers come from the west, from the south, from the north, and then from the east. Each time they see seven defenders, fire a volley of arrows, and retreat, chanting "Neves! Neves!"

The attack is over, but five more men have been killed. Is it still possible for the commander to place seven defenders along each wall, now that he has only 15 altogether?

In other words, can they survive that third, final day of attack?

Solutions on page 248

CHAPTER SEVEN
SUM OF THE PARTS

Mathematicians have two ways of solving puzzles: piecing together small bits of information to understand larger problems and breaking down complicated ideas into simpler parts. For example, *geometry* helps them understand how to combine certain shapes to make larger shapes or how to reduce certain shapes into smaller shapes. *Fractions* help them understand the functions of whole numbers. In each case, breaking something down in order to put it back together again can lead to a valuable understanding of basic mathematical principles.

Stamp Stumper

Start with a sheet of 24 stamps. Following the diagram below, tear out two sets of three stamps, making sure the stamps of each set remain joined. Tear out a third set, then a fourth set. How many sets, total, can you tear from the sheet?

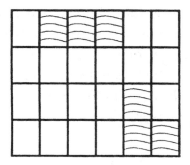

Broken Dishes

If you could put all the broken pieces back together in this drawing, how many dishes would you have?

Solutions on page 249

Cut the Pizza

A group of eight people walked into a restaurant and ordered a large pizza. The place was very busy, so when the pizza arrived, the waiter wanted to cut it up into eight even pieces as quickly as possible. He did this with only three straight cuts of his knife. Can you figure out how the waiter cut the pizza?

Solution on page 249

Fractured Fractions

In this puzzle, you must find two-thirds of three-fourths of five numbers.

Find 2/3 of 3/4 of 12.
Find 2/3 of 3/4 of 20.
Find 2/3 of 3/4 of 32.
Find 2/3 of 3/4 of 44.
Find 2/3 of 3/4 of 52.

Can you discover the trick to doing this quickly?

Divide the Time

By drawing only two lines, divide the clockface below so that the numbers in each section add up to the same sum.

Solutions on page 250

Parcels of Land

A landowner died and left a large, square piece of land to his wife and four sons. His wife received one fourth of the land (section A), and his sons had to parcel out the remaining three-fourths of land equally. Draw a picture showing how the landowner's sons divided the land. Remember, each of the four sections must be the same size and shape.

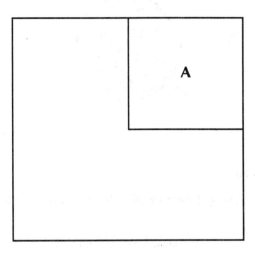

Four Lines in a Square

With a pencil and ruler, draw a square. Then draw four straight lines so that each line connects opposite sides of the square. Arrange your four lines so that you divide the square into as many sections as you can. Can you figure out the maximum number of sections you can make with only four lines?

Count the Blocks

Count the number of blocks in each arrangement. Assume that visible blocks rest on identically shaped hidden blocks, and that every arrangement is solid.

Solutions on page 250

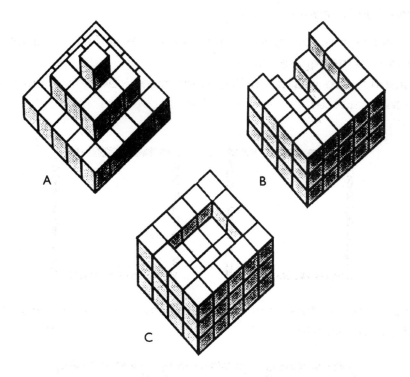

Sides, Edges & Corners

In the arrangement below, figure out how many blocks each numbered block touches. Blocks touch if any one of their sides, edges, or corners come in contact.

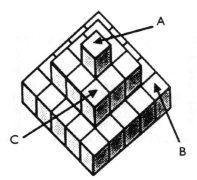

Solutions on page 250

Crayon Constructions

With 24 crayons, construct a large square. How many crayons does each side of the square contain?

Construct two squares of the same size. How many crayons are there to each side?

Now construct three squares of the same size. How many crayons are there to each side?

With one crayon to each side, you can make six identical small squares as shown.

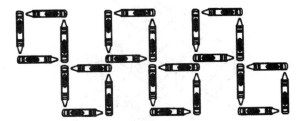

1. How do you determine how many squares of the same size you can construct with 24 crayons?
2. Now construct squares of different sizes, using 24 crayons.
A. With three crayons to a side, how many smaller squares do you get?
B. Construct squares with two crayons, maximum, to a side to make seven squares of two different sizes.
C. Construct seven *identical* squares with one crayon to a side.
D. Also, with one crayon to a side, construct eight and nine identical squares. How many larger squares does each design contain?

Clue: Squares can overlap and there'll be some bigger squares containing smaller ones.

Box the Dots

Divide the hexagon below so that each dot is in its own rectangular "box." All the boxes must be the same size, and there should not be any spaces between the boxes.

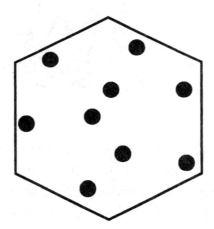

Hint: Think of the hexagon as a three-dimensional object.

Solutions on pages 250, 251

Logic Puzzles

At the root of all mathematical problem-solving is logical thinking. In fact, learning to think logically will help you solve nearly every kind of problem, mathematical or otherwise. Logical thinking begins with careful observation of the evidence, looking for consistent and inconsistent details, and then making a series of deductions that suggest a solution.

Tree-Chopping Contest

There was a race between six tree choppers to see who could chop down a tree first. Study the drawing below. Can you tell which chopper won first place in the contest? Which choppers won second, third, fourth, and fifth places? And finally, who came in last?

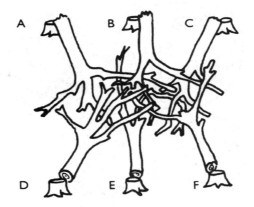

Filled Glasses

Of the six glasses below, three are filled with cranberry juice. By moving only one glass in the top row, make the top row resemble the bottom row.

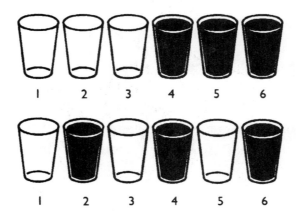

Solutions on page 252

Rare-Coin Thief

A shoplifter in a rare coin shop stole the oldest coin he could find, dated 260 B.C. If a rare coin is worth $30 for each year before Christ that it was minted, how much could the shoplifter get for his coin?

Fast Fishin'

If five fishermen catch five fish in five minutes, how long will it take fifty fishermen to catch fifty fish?

Solutions on page 252

213

Apricot Jam

After picking some apricots from your tree, you decide to make some delicious apricot jam. You cut up 10 pounds (4.5 kg) of apricots, blend them together, and place them on the stove. But suddenly you remember that you were supposed to add 1 teaspoon of lemon juice for every dozen apricots. Since you can no longer count the number of apricots in your mixture, how will you know how much lemon to add?

The Lumberjack's Brother

A lumberjack's brother died and left a million dollars to his only brother. However, the lumberjack never received any of the money even though it was legally paid out. How could this happen?

Chasing Shadows

Logical problem-solving always means a careful observation of the evidence. Look at the illustration of a tall tree seen from above and the shadow it casts at various times of day. Study the shadows carefully and identify four mistakes in the picture.

Solutions on page 252

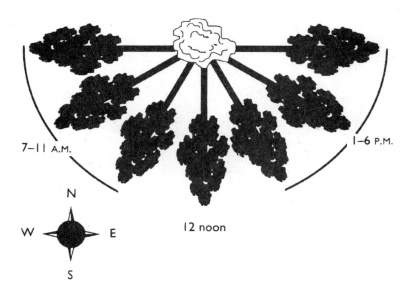

CHAPTER EIGHT
PENCIL-SHARPENING
MATH PUZZLES

IN TENTS

It is known that four officers are strategically located in four different tents that total thirty-two. Orders state that each horizontal, vertical, and diagonal row of four tents must quarter one officer. Which tents do the officers occupy?

Solution on page 252

THE THIRD DEGREE

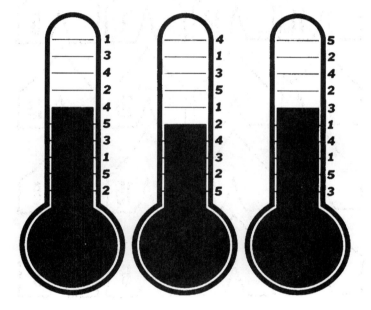

Your challenge is to balance the thermometers in this puzzle in such a way they all read an identical number. For each unit rise in any thermometer, one of the other thermometers must fill one unit, and vice versa.

Solution on page 252

MAD HATTER'S CAP SIZE

Here is a puzzle in which your challenge is to eliminate fractions. Add two or more of the cap sizes together to produce a whole number.

Solution on page 253

(Need a clue? Turn to page 221.)

TRUE TO ONE'S COLORS

The interior lines of this puzzle crisscross but do not intersect. Place the numbers one through nine in the nine colored circles to fulfill the following requirements: 1) Any set of three numbers which totals fifteen (there are eight) must include three different colors. 2) Numbers of consecutive value may not be directly linked by any passage.

Solution on page 253

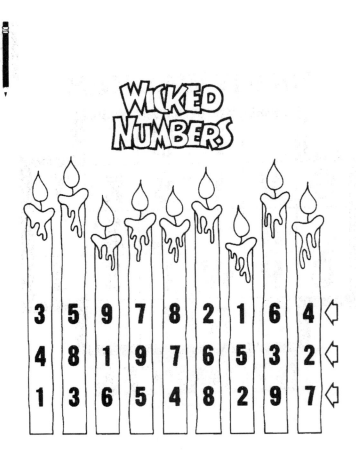

The numbers one through nine appear three times each in this puzzle. Your assignment is to blow out three candles which will total fifteen in each of the three horizontal rows. The three candles you select must carry the numbers one through nine. (No number may be used more than once.)

Solution on page 253

(Need a clue? Turn to page 224.)

NIGHTWALKER

DZOMPCEN

Position the eight remaining letters of the alphabet in the vacant squares of this puzzle to complete an alphabetical progression created by the moves of a chess knight.

Solution on page 253

Clue to the puzzle on page 218: Try "capsizing" on of the hats.

MAGIC
W□RD SQUARES

Each letter in this puzzle represents a different number from zero to nine. It is your challenge to switch these letters back to numbers in such a way that each horizontal, vertical, and diagonal row of three words totals the same number. Your total for this puzzle is 1446.

Solution on page 253

(Need A clue? Turn to page 225.)

TIC-TAC-TOPOLOGY

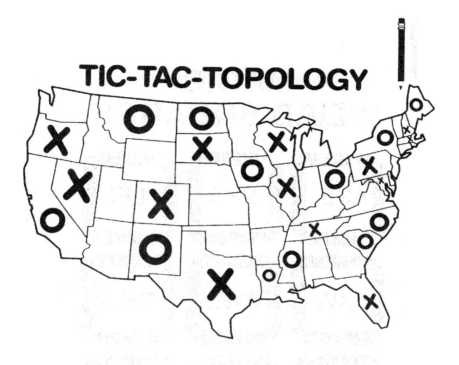

Here's a strategy game of topology for two players. Simply force your opponent to connect three or more states with their X's or O's and you win the game. Just as in tic-tac-toe, one player plays X and one player plays O. Players alternate positioning one of their marks per state until one player is forced to connect three or more states. In this sample game in progress, it is your move and challenge to position an O on the map in such a way that it will be impossible for your opponent to position an X without losing the game. Note: Only one X or O can be used to mark Michigan (a bridge is shown connecting both halves), but diagonally adjacent states, such as Arizona and Colorado, are not considered connected. You can enjoy playing this game with maps of other countries and continents.

Solution on page 253

HANG BY A THREAD

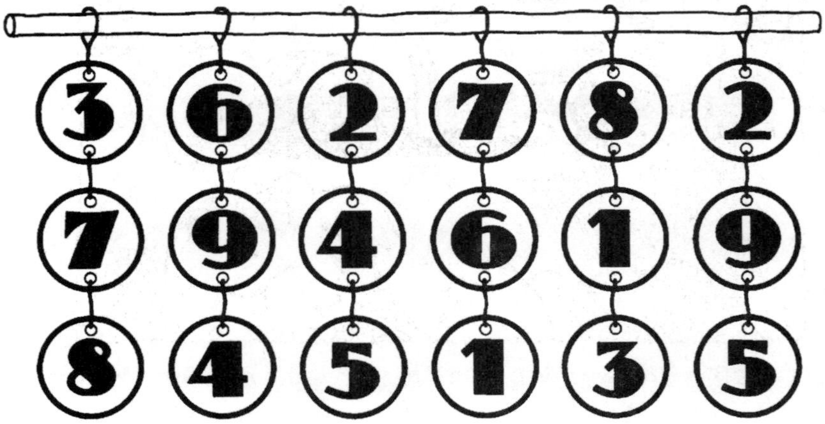

Disks arranged hanging by threads:

Row 1: 3 6 2 7 8 2
Row 2: 7 9 4 6 1 9
Row 3: 8 4 5 1 3 5

Each of the numbers one through nine appears twice in the eighteen disks that are hanging by threads. Your task is to cut the least number of threads so as to drop one set of numbers and leave nine disks hanging that reveal the remaining set of numbers from one to nine.

Solution on page 254

Clue to the puzzle on page 220: Start by blowing out the middle candle.

PIG STYMIE

Put nine pigs in eight pens.

Solution on page 254

Clue to the puzzle on page 222: APE = 473

GEOMETRACTS

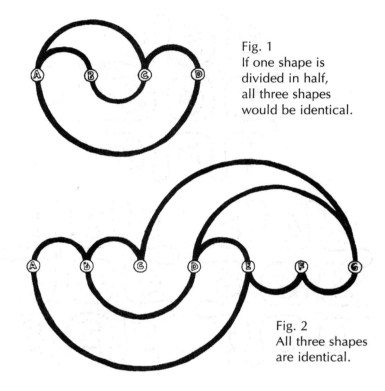

Fig. 1
If one shape is
divided in half,
all three shapes
would be identical.

Fig. 2
All three shapes
are identical.

Here are two distorted geometric figures. Both have been stretched in such a way that the original figure is unrecognizable at first glance. Your task is to straighten all the lines in each figure to reveal its original identity. The circled letters designate the intersection of two or more lines. Vital clues are given for each figure.

Solution on page 254

TIC-TAC-TOTAL

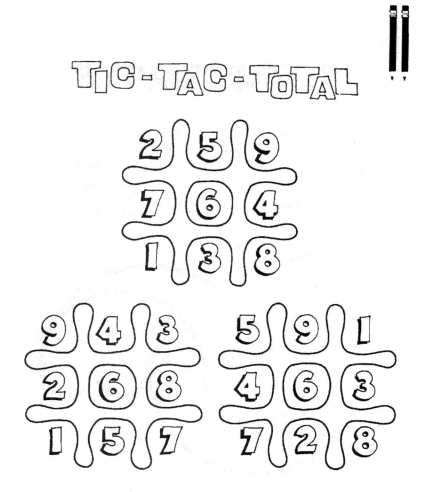

Your challenge in this puzzle is to circle a winning tic-tac-toe on each of the three game boards in the following manner: 1) One game must contain a diagonal win, one game must contain a horizontal win, and one game must contain a vertical win. 2) All numbers from one through nine must be circled in constructing these three winning lines.

Solution on page 254

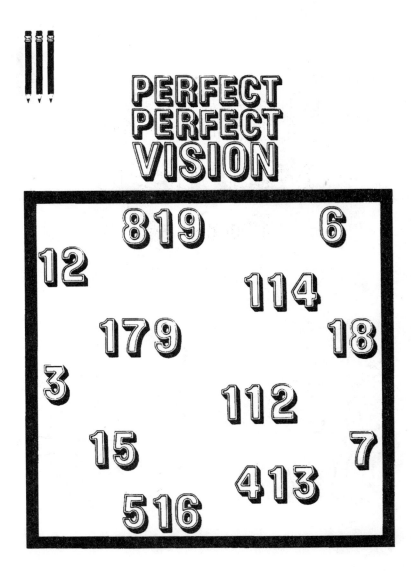

PERFECT PERFECT VISION

Using four straight lines, divide this square into nine pieces so that each piece totals the same number.

Solution on page 254

Chapter 9
Math Logic
Puzzles

Difficult Puzzles

Vegetable Soup Contest

Five people each bought 15 cans of vegetables for a soup contest. No one bought the same number of any kind, but 5 of one kind, 4 of another, 3 of another, and so on. Also, no vegetable was bought in the same quantity by any two people. Given all that, can you figure out how many cans of each vegetable each person bought and how much the purchases cost? Also, who won the contest for the tastiest soup?

1. The person who spent $6.43 bought 5 cans of asparagus and 3 cans of beans.
2. Lily spent the least amount of money, $1.66 less than T-bone. She bought 3 cans of carrots, 5 of peas, and 1 of corn.
3. Benny spent $1.20 on asparagus and $1.55 for corn and peas.
4. Joshua bought 2 cans of peas and spent $4.52 for his corn and carrots combined.
5. The person who won the contest bought 1 can of carrots and spent $7.42 total, 99¢ more than Benny.
6. T-bone spent the most. He bought 5 cans of corn, 4 of beans, and 1 of asparagus.

	corn	peas	carrots	asparagus	beans	amt. spent	winner
Benny							
Lily							
T-Bone							
Slim							
Joshua							

Shopping List	
corn	58¢
peas	39¢
carrots	44¢
asparagus	24¢
beans	64¢

See answers on page 243

Difficult Puzzles

Boxes

The sixteen boxes below are each worth the number inside. Their names are intersections of rows (letters) and columns (numbers), i.e., the lower left corner box is D-1 or 1-D. It is worth 9 points.

	1	2	3	4
A	11	6	15	3
B	5	8	12	10
C	16	1	14	7
D	9	2	13	4

Four boys playing a game are trying to make the most points by trading boxes. Everyone must have four boxes at all times. From the clues, how many points does each boy have at game's end?

1. Jeremy didn't own any of the boxes in the A row.
2. Boyd's highest number is A-3
3. B-2 and C-1 belong to the same boy, who isn't Bryce.
4. Bryce doesn't own any boxes in the 1 column.
5. On the last play of the game, Jeremy traded his 4-B for B-1.
6. D-2, A-2, and D-3 all belong to the same player.
7. C-1, B-3, and 4-D all belong to the same player.
8. Kevin's score was 4 higher than Boyd's.
9. Three of Boyd's boxes are in the A row.
10. Jeremy has just one box in the B row, which is B-1.

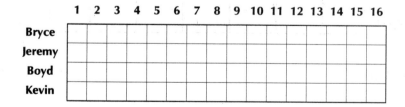

See answers on page 240

Foul Shots

Sometimes they make 'em, sometimes they don't! Using your excellent understanding of percentage, see if you can figure out the foul-shooting percentage for each of these six players this season. The highest is 83%. The lowest is 57%.

1. Player #34 had 102 successful shots, 30 fewer than the player who shot 71%.
2. The player with 57% (not #49 or #22) attempted 176 shots.
3. The player with 98 attempts shot 59%.
4. Player #27 shot 66%.
5. Player #12 had the fewest attempts and shot 80%.
6. The player with the highest percentage (not #18) made 38 fewer shots than #49.

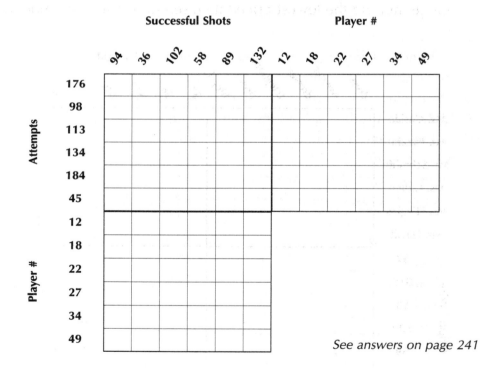

See answers on page 241

Garage Sale

Ms. Gaskin found a clothing item. A man who had searched for years bought an old dresser. All were happy to have saved money. Who bought what? What were the original and purchase prices?

1. The bicycle was bought at 50% off. The buyer's name starts with H.
2. Ms. Cullen bought the item priced at $15.00 for 4/5ths that amount.
3. The tires sold for $1.00 less than the asking price.
4. The item that sold for $0.50 was an article of clothing.
5. Mr. Pazzini spent $4.00 less than Ms. Cullen.
6. Ms. Higgins paid for her dress with a $20.00 bill and received $19.25 in change.
7. Ms. Gaskin spent less for her item than Mr. Schmidt, who spent less than Mr. Pazzini.
8. The item originally priced the highest didn't sell for the highest price, nor did the lowest-priced item sell for the lowest amount.

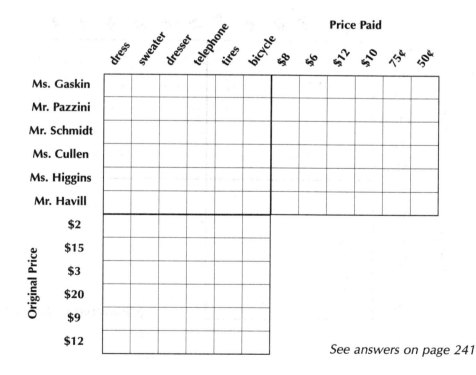

See answers on page 241

Great Pencil Sale

Four sixth-grade classes decided to sell pencils to raise money to go to a concert. Each class bought 500 pencils for $0.03 each (this cost must be deducted before any profit is made). They agreed that the class that made the most money (each class was allowed to charge any amount for their pencils) could sit in the front row at the concert.

Using the clues below, figure out how much profit each class made, and which class got to sit in the front row.

1. The least amount of profit was $11.30 less than the wining amount.
2. Mr. Pendip's class made $3.80 more in profit than the class that sold its pencils at 10 for 75¢.
3. The class that sold 219 pencils was not Mr. Pendip's.
4. Ms. Rimdrip's class sold its pencils for 7¢ more per pencil than Mr. Slimhip's class.

	Number Sold				Selling Price					
	219	375	413	500	5/40¢	10/75¢	10¢	15¢	$ profit	front row
Mr. Pendip										
Ms. Glenwhip										
Ms. Rimdrip										
Mr. Slimhip										

See answers on page 241

Hint: Use trial and error to determine the answer to clue #2 (the difference between Pendip's profit and Glenwhip's). Remember to deduct the original cost of the pencils from the profits when it is calculated.

Hidden Grades

Ms. Stonebelt told four of her best math students that their grades were hidden in the charts below. Using all the clues, see if you can figure out the grade each one received.

1. Dan's percentage is B + K - ½ C.
2. Bernard's grade is based on G + I + D – Dan's percentage plus sixty-five.
3. Jason earned a grade higher than Bernard. He scored 2E ÷ 3 + (½ J) – 2.
4. Dexter's grade, the only one of the four without a plus or a minus, was derived from:

$$(A + C - \{½ F\}) \times 1/5 \, G ÷ 10 + ½ J$$

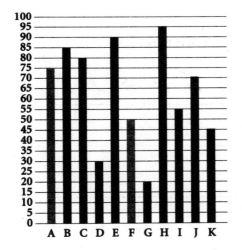

Grading System	
96-100	A
92-95	A-
89-91	B+
84-88	B
81-83	B-
77-80	C+
72-76	C
69-71	C-
62-68	D
0-61	F

See answers on page 241

Hundred-Miler

In a 100-mile bicycle race, Chet and his friends finished within 31 minutes of each other! From the clues, find each rider's last name, the bike color, the time each finished, and his average speed.

1. Both Dave and Seig rode over 6½ hours. Dave's bike is grey.
2. Day's bike, which beat Seig's green one, is blue.
3. The rider who rode for 6:32 hours was on a red bike.
4. Rick and the rider of the red bike both averaged under 16 mph.
5. The tan bike averaged 16.42.
6. The blue bike's rider is not Kurt, nor the one who took 6:40 hrs.
7. Brown, who rode in 6:09, is not Kurt or Bob.
8. Kurt's average beat Johns, who beat the green bike rider.

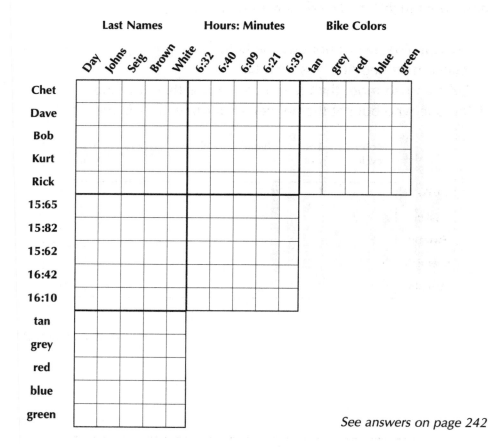

See answers on page 242

Motorcycle

Old Mrs. Frizzle needed a new motorcycle because her old one was worn out from so many trips to town. She summoned her five sons—Luke, Jake, Swizzle, Jeremiah, and Malcolm—and told them "Boys, I need a new motorcycle. It must be purple and it must have one extra tire. Also, I must have a new helmet, a new leather outfit, and new goggles. The one who finds me the best deal shall earn a handsome prize."

The sons met secretly and agreed that each would buy one of the five items and they would split the prize as follows: The one who bought the motorcycle would get 50% of the prize, the one who bought the tire would get 20%, the ones buying the outfit and the helmet would each get 12%, and the on e buying the goggles would get 6%.

See if you can deduce which son bought which of the five items, and how much Mrs. Frizzle gave as a prize.

1. Swizzle Frizzle did not buy the helmet.
2. Malcom earned 60¢ less than Jake.
3. Luke earned more than Jeremiah but less than Swizzle.
4 The one who bought the helmet—not Malcolm—Earned 90¢.

	Motor-cycle	Tire	Helmet	Outfit	Goggles	Prize Money
Luke						
Jake						
Swizzle						
Jeremiah						
Malcolm						

See answers on page 242

Hint: Start with clue #4, then go to clue #2.

Solutions

Bull's Eye

A. 16, 8, 1 (three arrows); **B.** 16, 2, 1 (three arrows); and **C.** 32, 8, 4, 2, 1, (five arrows).

You can form any whole number up to 63 on this target. Each number is a power of 2, which means that you can create any other whole number by combining numbers.

Jawbreakers

Three pennies. After the second penny, they would have either two yellow or two blue jawbreakers, or a yellow and a blue jawbreaker. A third penny would deliver a jawbreaker that had to match one of the colors.

Antsy Ant

Ten seconds. Since it takes the ant 12 seconds to cover the distance between 12 and 6 inches, it takes him 2 seconds to travel each inch. You can divide that distance into six 2-second time intervals.

Since it's a shorter distance between 6 inches and the 1-inch mark, you can divide that distance into only five 2-second intervals. So it takes the ant only 10 seconds to cover the remaining distance.

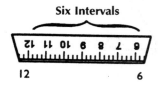 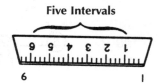

A Burned Receipt

$$
\begin{array}{r}
1425 \\
+\ 5421 \\
\hline
6666 \\
-\ 2374 \\
\hline
4292
\end{array}
$$

In the Old Cemetery

Mary was born in 1896, 1897, 1898, or 1899.

For example, if Mary were born January 5, 1897, and died on her birthday, January 5, 1903, she would have died on the first day of her seventh year. The year 1900 was not a leap year, since it was centesimal (ending in 00); so, there were no leap years in Mary's lifetime. Thus, she lived exactly six years of 365 days each, or 2,190 days.

If her brother John were born January 5, 1903, and died the day before his birthday, January 4, 1909, it would have only been the last day of his *sixth* year. However, during John's lifetime there would have been two leap years, 1904 and 1908. Thus, although he lived six years minus one day, two years had an extra day, making his lifetime a total of 2,191 days—one day longer than Mary's.

For this to be possible, Mary must have been born no earlier than March 1, 1896, since her last year was expressed in a single digit.

Magic Squares

The magic constant for a fifth-order square is 65.

More Magic Shapes

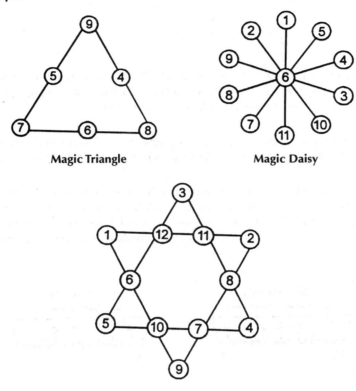

Magic Triangle   Magic Daisy

Magic Star

Ben Franklin's Wheel

Missing numbers, clockwise starting above the circled band numbers are: Band 1: 73, 30, 46 Band 2: 24, 47, 63   Band 3: 64, 39, 48   Band 4: 17, 70, 33   Band 5: 66, 18   Band 6: 19, 51, 36, 52 Band 7: 75, 28, 44   Band 8: 26, 61, 42.

The magic number that the rings add up to is 360, the number of degrees in a circle.

The Chimes of Big Ben

It takes 7½ seconds. You can illustrate the chiming of Big Ben like this.

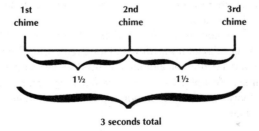

The first chime accounts for the interval from the first to the second chime. The second chime accounts for the interval from the second to the third chime and ends with the third chime. Therefore, you must divide the 3 seconds in half since only two intervals exist for three chimes, averaging 1½ seconds per interval.

At 6 o'clock, you would have five intervals totaling 7½ seconds as shown.

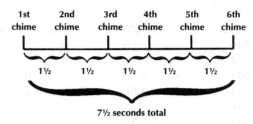

Count the Streetlights

It's 660 yards. There are 23 lamps on one side and 22 on the other side. There are 22 gaps between 23 lamps; therefore, the street is 22 times 30 yards long, or 660 yards.

Weighing In

The cube is 6 pounds, the pyramid 3 pounds, and the sphere 2 pounds.

Auction

Irene Black bought cheese ($5). Denise Green bought pie ($4). Duane Grey bought coffee ($7). Dan White bought cake ($6). Elroy Brown bought fruit ($3.50).

Biology Class

Kate adopted Willy, the mole (18 cm). Kristen adopted Weldon, the ladybug (1.3 cm). Kurt adopted Walter, the fly (1 cm). Kristi adopted Wendy, the rat (14 cm). Kyle adopted Warren, the bat (11 cm). Kevin adopted Wanda, the hamster (23 cm).

Boxes

Bryce had 2, 6, 10, and 13 for 31 total.
Jeremy had 1, 5, 9, and 14 for 29 total.
Boyd had 3, 7, 11, and 15 for 36 total.
Kevin had 4, 8, 12, and 16 for 40 total.

Chicken Mountain

Chicken-grading formula results: Saffola 242.5; McSanders 257.6 (winner); McPlume 172.2; McCombe 224.9; Poularde 196.6.

Chocolate Chip Cookies

Ms. Effie Bundt puts in 5 chips and bakes for 16 min 17 sec.
Ms. Ruby Strudel puts in 7 chips and bakes for 17 min 7 sec.
Ms. Thelma Spicer puts in 8 chips and bakes for 16 min 9 sec.
Ms. Miriam Applestreet puts in 9 chips and bakes for 17 min.
Ms. Georgia Honeydew puts in 10 chips, baking for 17 min 8 sec.

Coast to Coast

The route that Jacques and Chi Chi traveled took them in order to: Phoenix, Los Angeles, San Francisco, Portland, Salt Lake City, Denver, Dallas, St. Louis, Chicago, Pittsburgh, and finally to Washington, D.C.

Coffee

Max drinks 4 cups, with 2 sugars, no milk.
Doris drinks 5 cups, with 1 sugar, milk.
Blizzo drinks 1 cup, with no sugar, no milk.
Jan drinks 6 cups, with 6 sugars, milk.
Boris drinks 8 cups, with 4 sugars, no milk.

Decimal Ruler

The lengths of the lines are: **a** 3.3; **b** 1.3; **c** 3.9; **d** 2.8; **e** 0.6; **f** 3.8; **g** 1.8.

Destry's Missing Numbers

The square are: **A** 22.34; **B** 11.93; **C** 25.17; **D** 13.47; **E** 25.71.

Dog Apartments

Name	Apt. No.	Food/Week	Baths/Month
MacTavish	408	2 lbs.	9
Chico	103	10 lbs.	3
Ivan	609	8 lbs.	12
Wilfred	512	4 lbs.	2
Taz	221	12 lbs.	6
Spunky	341	6 lbs.	4

E.F. Bingo

Wanda won when the $^{16}/_{18}$ths fraction was called.

Famous Person

J O H N   F   K E N N E D Y

Fishing

Fred, using worms, caught one fish. Sammy, using dry flies, caught three fish. Torkel, using eggs, caught two fish. Joe, using flatfish, caught no fish at all.

Flighty Decimals

In the square:	4.39	4.01	2.60	1.42	total: 12.42
In the circle:	5.20	1.16	.07	.03	total: 6.46
In the rectangle:	3.71	1.01	.72	.30	total: 5.74

Foul Shots

Player #12 made 36 foul shots out of 45 attempts, for 80%.
Player #18 made 58 foul shots out of 98 attempts, for 59%.
Player #22 made 94 foul shots out of 113 attempts, for 83%.
Player #27 made 89 foul shots out of 134 attempts, for 66%.
Player #34 made 102 foul shots out of 176 attempts, for 57%.
Player #49 made 132 foul shots out of 184 attempts, for 71%.

Garage Sale

Ms. McGaskin bought the sweater for $0.50; original price $3.
Mr. Pazzini bought the tires for $8.00; originally $9.
Mr. Schmidt bought the dresser for $6; originally $12.
Ms. Cullen bought the telephone for $12; originally $15.
Ms. Higgins bought the dress for $0.75; originally $2.
Mr. Havill bought the bicycle for $10; originally $20.

Great Pencil Sale

Mr. Pendip sold 413 at 10¢ each for a $26.30 profit (front row seats).
Mr. Glenwhip sold 500 at 10 for 75¢, for a profit of $22.50.
Ms. Rimdrip sold 219 at 15¢ each, for a profit of $17.85.
Mr. Slimhip sold 375 at 5 for 40¢ for a profit of $15.00.

Heather's Garden

Heather has: 3 rows of carrots, 4 rows of cabbages, 1 row of turnips, 2 rows of pole beans, 5 rows of spinach, and 6 rows of cucumbers.

Hidden Grades

Dan scored 90 (B+); Bernard got 80 (C+); Jason got the highest grade, 93 (A–); Dexter got 87 (B).

Hundred Miler
Chet Brown rode the tan bike in 6:09 hours to average 16.42.
Dave Johns rode the grey bike in 6:39 hours to average 15.65.
Bob Day rode the blue bike in 6:21 hours to average 16.10.
Kurt White rode the red bike in 6:32 hours to average 15.82.
Rick Seig rode the green bike in 6:40 hours to average 15.62.

Jump Rope
Danielle made 12 jumps; Gary made 9 jumps; Jan jumped 20 times; Arnie jumped 17 times; and Ruth made 25 jumps before missing a jump.

Lunch at Paul's
Paul brought the olives and bought the coffee for $2.75.
Julie brought the cake and bought the cheese for $2.70.
Sandra brought the pickles and bought the mayonnaise for $2.18.
Diane brought the fruit and bought the chicken for $4.80.
Wally brought the salad and bought the bread for $4.17.

Mathathon
The girls defeated the boys 80 to –10.

Motorcycle
Luke bought the helmet and got 90¢. Jake bought the tire and got $1.50. Swizzle bought the motorcycle and earned $3.75. Jeremiah bought the goggles and earned 45¢. Malcolm bought the outfit and got 90¢. The "handsome prize" was $7.50.

Notes: The puzzle "key" is the prize money promised by old Mrs. Frizzle. Knowing from clue #4 that 90¢ represents 12%, you divide $.90 by .12 to get $7.50, the "handsome prize." Then, you can determine that 50% of $7.50 is $3.75, that 20% is $1.50, and that 6% is 45¢. From clue #2, you know that Malcolm can have only 90¢, because any other amount plus 60¢ would not total any of the other amounts. Therefore, Jake has $1.50, meaning he bought the tire.

Mountain Climb
Dacon climbed Mirre (7500-foot elevation). Drakon climbed Old Baldy (4500). Macom climbed Goat (8000). Bacon climbed Sleepy (9000). Jake climbed Raleigh (11,000).

Mountain Race
Andy Stiller climbs Mt. Stewart carrying 20 lbs.
Gerald Brown climbs Mt. Morgan carrying 40 lbs.
Dale Dorsey climbs Mt. Waring carrying 50 lbs.
Paul Anderson climbs Mt. McIntire carrying 30 lbs.
Jim McGee climbs Mt. Picard carrying 10 lbs.

Multiplication Jeopardy

Sue Jensen	8 x 15	=	120
June James	9 x 16	=	144
Dale Johnson	5 x 14	=	70
Neil Johns	7 x 18	=	126
Tina Jones	11 x 13	=	143

Ned's Newspaper Route
The Joneses live in the green house and get a *daily only* (clue #4).
The Johnsons live in the blue house and get a Sunday only.
The Smiths live in the grey house and get a Sunday only.
The Browns live in the white house and get both daily and Sunday.
The Simpsons live in the yellow house and also get both papers.

Old House

The Barneses lived 11 years in the red-painted house.
The Carpenters lived 44 years in the green-painted house.
The Lewises lived 5 years in the blue-painted house.
The Parkers lived 2 years in the yellow-painted house.
The Smiths lived 22 years in the brown-painted house.
The Warners lived 4 years in the white-painted house.

Play Ball

Teddie has a white soccer ball that weighs 16 oz.
Teresa has an orange golf ball that weighs 1.5 oz.
Toddy has a yellow Ping-Pong ball that weighs .8 oz.
Tanya has a green tennis ball that weighs 2 oz.
Tom has a brown basketball that weighs 22 oz.
Tillie has a red football that weighs 15 oz.

Pocket Change

Alex started with $4 and ended with 40¢. Scott started with $3 and ended with 95¢. Dan started with $2 and ended with 10¢. Jim started with $1 and ended with 70¢. Duane started with $2 and ended with $1.65.

Potato Chips

Elmo Glitzwhizzle ate 18 bags. Gazelda Kettledrummel ate 6 bags. Amos Grugenminer ate 12 bags. Gerald Crackenberry ate 9 bags. Sally Witteyspooner ate 3 bags. Hubert Jones ate 24 bags!

Queen Rachel's Bridge Toll

Chiquita wears black shoes and pays 18¢ bridge toll.
Cindy wears blue shoes and pays 36¢ bridge toll.
Kurt wears red shoes and pays 14¢ bridge toll.
Taber wears white shoes and pays 38¢ bridge toll.
Caleb wears green shoes and pays 24¢ bridge toll.

Skateboard Contest

Jimmy Cooper rode 8 blocks, from Elm St. Sally Mander rode 3, from Main St. Lenny Linden rode 11, from Chestnut Ave. Roger Chapman rode 7, from Acorn Dr. Kenny Lyle rode 1, from 11th St.

Temperature

The lowest temperature is at the 10:30 a.m. reading. The drop in temperature then is due to all the open doors as the students take their morning break.

Vegetable Soup Contest

	Corn	Peas	Carrots	Asparagus	Beans	Spent
Benny	2	1	4	5	3	$6.43
Lily	1	5	3	4	2	$6.09
T-Bone	5	3	2	1	4	$7.75
Slim	3	4	1	2	5	$7.42 (winner)
Joshua	4	2	5	3	1	$6.66

128

129

6 x 6 =　9 boards
4 x 4 = 25 boards
2 x 2 = 49 boards
　　　　83 total

130

131

132

133

134

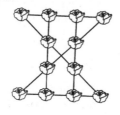

135

136 Reflections and rotations
also correct.

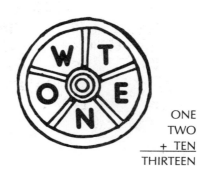

ONE
TWO
+ TEN
THIRTEEN

137

138

139 Eliminate W, K, and E. Substitute the Roman numerals V, X, and L.

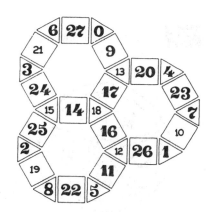

140 From the dark star, proceed to 7, 3, 12, 6, 10, 2, 5, 8, 1, 9, 11, 4, white star. Reverse order also correct.

141 SIX equals VI.

142 One of several possible solutions.

143 Keys needed: 1, 3, 5.

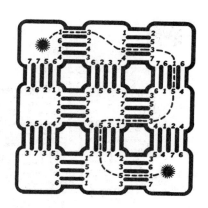

144

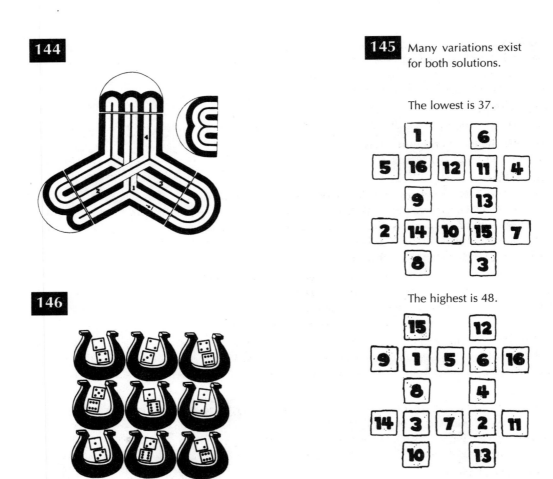

146

145 Many variations exist for both solutions.

The lowest is 37.

		1			6		
5	16	12	11	4			
		9			13		
2	14	10	15	7			
		8			3		

The highest is 48.

		15			12		
9	1	5	6	16			
		8			4		
14	3	7	2	11			
		10			13		

Sox Unseen

Sam has to take out 3 sox; then he's bound to get two of the same color.

Gloves Galore!

This is trickier than the sox, because some gloves fit on the right hand and some on the left. You *might* pick out all 12 left hand gloves, one right after the other, but then the next must make a pair; so you need to take 13 gloves to make sure.

Birthday Hugs

Each girl kisses 3 others; so it looks like 4 x 3 = 12 kisses, but that would be counting Jenny kissing Janey as one kiss, and Janey kissing Jenny as another, counting each kiss twice.

Actually, there are six kisses altogether.

Gold Star answer: Jabberwocky *by Lewis Carroll.*

Sticky Shakes

Same trick as with the kisses. Either you can say each of the 7 shakes with six; so the total is a half of 7 x 6, or 21 shakes. Or you can say John shakes with 6; Jack shakes with 5 others (don't count John again); Jake shakes with 4 others, and so on. The total number of handshakes is 6 + 5 + 4 + 3 + 2 + 1 = 21.

The Wolf, the Goat, and the Cabbage

Take the goat across. Go back; take the wolf across, and bring the goat back. Take the cabbage across. Go back for the goat. Then the goat is never alone with either the wolf or the cabbage.

Floating Family

The two kids row across. One brings the boat back. Then Mom rows across, and the other kid brings the boat back. Both kids row across. One brings the boat back. Then Dad rows across, and the second kid takes the boat back to collect her brother.

Slippery Slopes

Ten days. After 9 days and 9 nights, she is at 9000 feet. On the 10th day she climbs 3000 feet to the summit!

The Long and the Short of the Grass

They mowed the grass on 9 Saturdays, earning 9 x $2 = $18, and missed 6 Saturdays, losing 6 x $3 = $18.

Sugar Cubes

1. The first trick is to count the zeros! To find out how big the big cube is you need to find the cube root of a million. A million has six zeros—1,000,000—so its cube root must have one third of six—two zeros—100.

    The cube root of a million is a hundred. So the big cube is 100 cubes long, 100 wide, and 100 high. Each cube is half an inch; so 100 cubes is 50 inches, or just over 4 feet long. You would not fit this under a table, but it would go easily in a garage.

2. This time you are making a square; so you need the square root of a million. A million has six zeros; its square root must have half six; that is, three zeros—1000. The square root of a million is a thousand. So the big square on the ground is 1000 half inches long and 1000 half inches wide. 1000 half inches is 500 inches; dividing by 12 will give you 41 feet 8 inches. You could fit this square on a tennis court.

3. The pile is a million cubes high; a million half inches, or 500,000 inches. Divide by 12 for 41,666 feet 8 inches. This is higher than Mount Everest. You could make one pile as high as Mount Everest and one as high as Mount Adams, and still have a few cubes left over!

Crackers!

This is surprisingly easy; the trick is to add a plain cracker. Then Marty has a choice of 2—mayo or plain. Marty and Jake have a choice of 4; when Hank arrives they have a choice of 8, since the number of choices doubles with each new person. So when Hank comes there will be 16 choices—or 15 spreads. When Charlie is there they'll have 32 choices—31 spreads. And Fred will bring the total to 64 choices—63 spreads!

Crate Expectations

There are many different patterns that work, but here is an easy one to remember. Now try ten bottles!

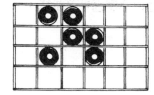

Take It Away!

If you are left with 3, you must lose, because you can't take all three, but if you take 1 your opponent will take 2, and if you take 2 your opponent will take 1. So the first rule for winning is, to *try to leave your opponent with three items!* You can also win if you leave 6, because after leaving 6 you can always leave 3 next turn. And you can win if you leave 9. Can you spot the pattern?

Oddwins

This Oddwins game is so tricky that even math professors haven't been able to find a way to always win. So here's your chance. See if you can master it—then let *us* know!

Witches' Brew

The pan holds 3 pints; fill it and then fill the jug from it. The jug holds 1 pint; so that leaves exactly 2 pints in the pan. Pour it into the cauldron and carry on cooking!

Witches' Stew

Fill the pitcher to the brim. Use it to fill the pot, which leaves just 2 pints in the pitcher. Empty the pot back into the bucket. Pour the 2 pints from the pitcher into the pot. Fill the pitcher again. Now carefully top off the pot from the pitcher. This will take exactly 1 pint, because there are 2 pints in it already. That leaves exactly 4 pints in the pitcher—pour them into the cauldron!

Cookie Jars

Joe has no cookies; so this puzzle is easy. If Ken gave him one, he'd have a total of one; so if they have the same number, Ken must also have one left. Therefore Ken must have two to begin with.

Fleabags

Captain has two fleas; Champ has four.

Frisky Frogs

Freda steps, Fred hops over her, Frank steps, Freda hops, Francine hops, Fergie steps, Fred hops, Frank hops, Frambo hops, Freda steps, Francine hops, Fergie hops, Frank steps, Frambo hops, Fergie steps—and they are all across, in 15 moves.

Leaping Lizards

Try using these guide rules; 1. Don't move a boy next to another boy—or a girl next to another girl—until you reach the other side; 2. Step if you can, hop if you can't step; 3. Once you have moved a girl, keep moving girls till you have to stop; then move boys till you have to stop. The quickest has 23 leaps.

Wiener Triangles

You can make 5 triangles, including the big one round the outside.

The Power of Seven

After 4 have been killed, and there are 20 left, the commander must put 2 in each corner tower, and 3 along each side wall.

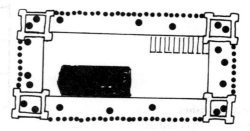

The Power of Seven continues

Yes, they can survive the final attack. Four defenders go in one corner tower, three in all the others. 15 men make 7 on each side!

Old MacDonald

All the 12 wings must have belonged to turkeys, because pigs don't usually have any; so he must have had 6 turkeys (with 2 wings each). The 6 turkeys must have had 12 legs; leaving 12 legs for the pigs, and since each pig has four legs, that makes 3 pigs. So Old MacDonald had 3 pigs and 6 turkeys.

Old Mrs. MacDonald

Mrs. MacDonald counted 12 heads, so she must have had 12 animals. If they had all been chickens she would have had 24 legs; if they had all been cows she would have had 48 legs. The difference between these two is 24, or 2 legs more than 24 for each cow. She counted 34 legs. That is 10 more than 24; so she must have had 5 cows.

Check; 5 cows = 5 heads; 7 chickens = 7 heads;
total 5 + 7 = 12 heads.
And 5 cows = 20 legs; 7 chickens = 14 legs;
total 20 + 14 = 34 legs.

Tennis Tournament

In a knockout tournament, every player has to lose one match—except the winner, who loses none. So the total number of matches is one less than the number of players. If 27 enter, there will be 26 matches.

Stamp Stumper

There are eight sets, however you wish to divide them.

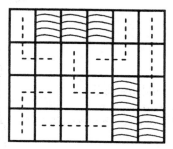

Broken Dishes

You'd have six dishes.

Cut the Pizza

Two cuts will make no more than four pieces. A third cut will make no more than seven pieces. So, in order to make eight pieces from three cuts, you need to think three-dimensionally and stack the four quater-pieces on top of one another.

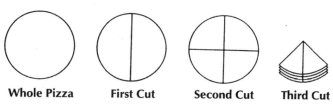

Whole Pizza   **First Cut**   **Second Cut**   **Third Cut**

Fractured Fractions

Since all the numbers are multiples of 4, you can solve the problem by first finding three-fourths of the number and then finding two-thirds of that answer.

For the numger 12, for example: $3/4$ of 12 is 9; $2/3$ of 9 is 6.

The answer will always be half the original number.

Divide the Time

When you add all the numbers on the face of the clock you get a sum of 78. Since two intersecting lines always make four sections, and since 78 cannot be divided evenly into four sections, the lines you draw must not intersect. Instead, you must draw two parallel lines that divide the clockface into three sections.

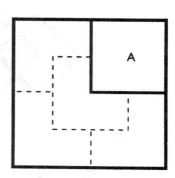

$$11 \quad + \quad 12 \quad + \quad 1 \quad + \quad 2 \quad = \quad 26$$
$$10 \quad + \quad 9 \quad + \quad 3 \quad + \quad 4 \quad = \quad 26$$
$$8 \quad + \quad 7 \quad + \quad 6 \quad + \quad 5 \quad = \quad 26$$

Parcels of Land

Divide the original sqare into fourths. One-fourth (square A) was willed to the landowner's wife. Since there were three squares left to be subdivided among the four sons, removing one-fourth of each remaining square leads to the arrangement at right.

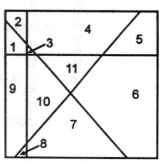

Four Lines in a Square

You can draw a maxium of eleven sections in the square using only four straight lines. To do this, each line must intersect all the other lines.

Count the Blocks

The number of blocks are: (A) 35, (B) 49, and (C) 54.

Sides, Edges & Corners

Block A touches nine other blocks, block B touches four other blocks, and block C touches 13 other blocks.

Crayon Constructions

1. How do you determine how many squares of the same size you can construct with 24 crayons?

To find out how many squares, divide 24 by one of its multiples 2, 4, 6, or 8, and then divide the result (quotient) by 4 for the total number of squares. For example:

$$24 \div 2 = 12$$
$$12 \div 4 = 3$$

Or, three squares with two crayons to a side.

$$24 \div 3 = 8$$
$$8 \div 4 = 2$$

Or, two squares with three crayons to a side.

2A. Two squares with three crayons to a side give you one smaller square.

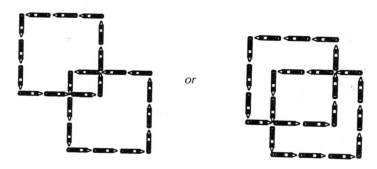

or

2B.

2C.

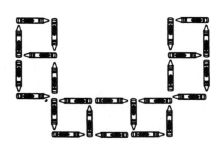

2D. One larger square.

Two larger squares.

Five larger squares.

In all cases, the correct answer depends on having the minimum number of crayons on the perimeter. The most economical area is the one with the smallest perimeter.

Box the Dots
Here's how you can box the dots.

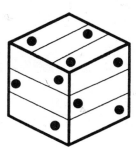

Tree-Chopping Contest
In first place was E; second place, C; third place, A; fourth place, B; fifth place, F; and last place, D.

Filled Glasses
A common-sense solution is in order here: pour the cranberry juice in glass #5 into glass #2 and return empty glass #5 to its original position.

Rare-Coin Thief
Zero. The coin is counterfeit because the term B.C. ("Before Christ") makes no sense on an ancient coin. How could the minter know that Christ would be born 260 years *after* he minted the coin?

Fast Fishin'
Five minutes. Each fisherman takes five minutes to catch a fish no matter how many fishermen are fishing. The time element remains constant and does not influence the outcome of this problem.

Apricot Jam
Count the pits.

The Lumberjack's Brother
The lumberjack was female.

Difficulties in figuring this one out have to do with making a false connection between gender and an appropriate job. This leads to the mistaken assumption that all lumberjacks must be men.

Chasing Shadows
1. The sun rises in the east, so the 7 A.M. to 11 A.M. morning shadows would be to the left of the tree, not to the right.
2. At 12 noon there would be no shadow since the sun is directly overhead.
3. The sun sets in the west, so the late afternoon and evening shadows would be to the right of the tree, not to the left.
4. The shadows should not all be the same length, since they shorten as the day approaches 12 noon, then lengthen again in the late afternoon and evening.

216

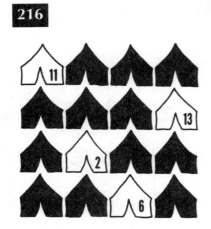

217

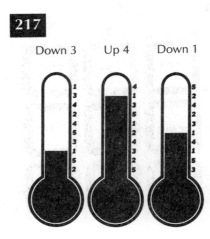

218 This puzzle is solved by turning over, or "capsizing" the 9/8 hat. Now, 8/6 + 10/6 = 3.

219

220

221

O	F	U	Z		
G	V	Y	B	K	T
N	A	P	E	X	C
Q	H	W	L	S	J
	M	R	I	D	

222

473	734	239
248	482	716
725	230	491

223

224 Cut four threads.

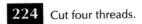
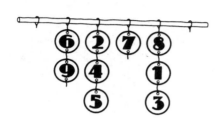

226

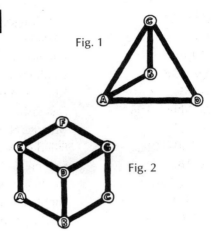

Fig. 1

Fig. 2

225

227

228 Each square totals twenty.

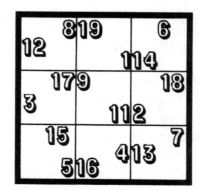

Index